R.I.P. Off!

R.I.P. Off!

or
The British Way of Death

Ken West

Matador
9 Priory Business Park,
Wistow Road, Kibworth Beauchamp,
Leicestershire. LE8 0RX
Tel: (+44) 116 279 2299
Fax: (+44) 116 279 2277
Email: books@troubador.co.uk
Web: www.troubador.co.uk/matador

ISBN 978 1783061 488

British Library Cataloguing in Publication Data.
A catalogue record for this book is available from the British Library.

Printed and bound in the UK by TJ International, Padstow, Cornwall
Typeset by Troubador Publishing Ltd, Leicester, UK

Matador is an imprint of Troubador Publishing Ltd

With gratitude to Carlisle City Council and the people who supported the revolution in the British way of death.

To funeral directors who perform a difficult job; secretly; expensively.

CHAPTER ONE

The Men in Black

CHAPTER ONE

The Men in Black

It was the yellow post-it notes that did it. Graham had no fear of the dead; but the living made him very nervous. The machinations of humans, those higher creatures supposedly in possession of a soul, were sometimes too dire to stomach. These were his thoughts just after he arrived at a house to collect the body of a dead father. The daughter opened the door and welcomed him, but as he entered the hall he was confronted by a beautiful photograph of the Lake District, framed and mounted on the wall. He had been to this dramatic spot overlooking Derwentwater. It's a common enough picture in Cumbrian homes, but it's the little yellow post-it note stuck in the centre of Derwentwater that surprised him; written on it is the Christian name 'Barbara'. As he passed through the hall behind the daughter, he is momentarily aware of more yellow stickers, one to each item, on a mantelpiece clock, even on a rug. But his professional focus instantly returned as he was confronted by the dead man, reclined in an armchair. The armchair has its own yellow sticker. As he neared this he could see 'Cynthia' neatly written on it; she was the second of three daughters. The father's estate had been apportioned; no need for a solicitor with the invention of the post-it note, thought Graham. He studied the vacant face of the corpse symbolically staring up at the ceiling;

it was as if the eyes knew that it was the only part of the room without a yellow sticker.

That evening he was at his first BALU meeting, and he felt edgy. As he entered the room and first saw the assemblage of funeral directors, the images from his love of cheap crime thrillers was to the fore. The word mafia sprung to mind. It was too obvious to be ignored. The preponderance of black suits was the visual stimuli, and even where a man had removed the black jacket, there beneath lay the black waistcoat. It was the reptile thing of repeatedly sloughing off skins and yet, underneath, it remained the same creature. He imagined he was looking into Burtons, a room full of suits, but, unlike Burtons, none were modelled for young, lithe male bodies. These were filled with a generous torso; the arms fill the white shirt; the buttocks the pants; nothing in the dress is slack or loose. Funeral directors never look creased.

Although Graham was new to funeral directing, he was already aware that they were intensely conscious of their image. In the room he could already pick out a pair or two of sunglasses, even though they were in the depths of winter. Although these were his colleagues, he was tense because the relationship was uneasy. They might look relaxed and affable, but each and every one worried about the words that might inadvertently escape during the meeting. He had no such worries, because he would not speak. Nobody at his firm had actually told him to keep mum; his newness and lowly rank did not qualify him to speak. He was aware that the major reason for this caution was that none of the gang wanted to share information; the number of funerals, the prices, the established rituals and practices. It was too easy to give this away as part of casual talk. Unlike the war, it's not the walls that have ears, but every other funeral director in the room.

His mind returned to the mafia. Since starting the work he felt as if a contract was out, not on an individual but on those whom the profession had disembodied; the bereaved. He had quickly realised that the word bereaved was never used, it was too humane and made them seem too real and too vulnerable. The contract demanded the language of euphemism; the bereaved are clients and the dead asleep or at rest. Clients could be discussed with impunity and this contrived language was their business speak. He had already been instructed that the deceased was always at repose, or at peace, but never dead. Only an incompetent funeral director would imply that somebody had failed to keep the person alive. Graham smiled as he recalled a doctor recently saying, "Your father's treatment has had a negative outcome!"

Graham was getting to know funeral directing. As he moved around the room and was introduced to other members of BALU, he recognised the same air of benevolence that he had first encountered on entering the profession. Even a casual observer could not fail to go away with the impression that these sombre professionals bestowed their services for free; that the clients never receive a bill.

For him, any doubt that these were quasi-mafia was beyond question. As the meeting progressed, it became evident that there is a common enemy, a foe. Graham knew that, professionally, they had to despise government, especially their Social Fund funeral payment, and the Office of Fair Trading, but this was different, it was personal. The offender was an individual, a person by the name of Ben West.

Graham had heard the crack, so this man was not new to

him. Ben offended on two counts. Firstly, he was an offcomer. He was born so far south another half mile and he would have drowned in the Solent near Southampton. Cumbrians, as with so many rural people, pin a name on recent interlopers, those who arrived in the last hundred years. They are offcomers, a neat appellation intended to highlight their lack of local family. This could be reinforced with suitable word associations; 'from down South' was typical, or something implying weirdness such as 'he is into art'. Secondly, Ben was an advocate of change and this, especially from an offcomer, was intolerable. Funeral directors hated change even more than they hated the increase in octogenarians. Change was anathema to them, they still liked to masquerade as Victorians in top hats and silver topped canes, then charge fancy Belgravia prices to blunt Northerners; not that they knew where Belgravia was.

It amused Graham, the way these BALU members disliked offcomers and yet it was perverse; they did not identify the Scots as offcomers. There was an unspoken correlation; the genuine offcomer was English, and it heightened the further south they were born!

Graham was no great lover of the Scots, but even he was aware of the ambivalence in Cumbrians to points north and south. Their capital, Carlisle is so far north that many of the English consider it to be in Scotland, and so it was in past times. It swayed too and fro between Scotland and England, but ultimately ended up just south of the border. That, they considered, gave them the status of the English, with the invisible border separating them from low fruit intake, alcohol poisoning, string vests, and early death.

The funeral directors were meeting in a hotel in a small

town south of Carlisle. Graham, despite his naivety, knew that on a day to day basis, there was much resentment between the members. The small rural family firms resented the larger family firms in Carlisle. The rural firms used old Ford hearses in two tone, black and rust! The bigger firms might operate a flashy Jaguar based hearse, and they all charged much higher prices. Conversely, staff at the larger firms saw the little rural enterprises as pathetic, old fashioned Micawber outfits, often part-time builders and carpenters, who had no understanding of marketing and promotion. Bizarrely, in the incestuous world of funeral directing, so many of the staff had been poached between firms over the years, it was impossible to recall who had worked for whom, and where allegiances really lay. But even in his naivety, Graham could see that when change was afoot, they stood shoulder pad to shoulder pad. Those few funeral directors, who would not join BALU, were deemed to support Ben and considered traitors.

Ben West was going to attend this meeting later, and Graham wondered if this was the cause of the tension. He was a new member of the Cumbrian Branch of BALU, the British Association of Licensed Undertakers. As a new member he was aware that the association's name had been carefully chosen to suggest a degree of professionalism. This was because they were intensely conscious of the ease in which anybody could be a funeral director. They could operate without any licensing or control, and needed no qualifications or registration.

As he looked around, Graham recognised the four principal funeral directors in the room and a few of the lesser players. These latter players worked in the remoter parts of Cumbria but their nearest crematorium was Carlisle, where he occasionally saw them. There was an undocumented and unspoken hierarchy based on the assumed number of funerals they each carried out, although actual numbers were never openly stated. The exception to this was Ronson Neal, whose patch was a small town where few people died. He sat at the top of the hierarchy simply by virtue of acting as secretary of the Cumbrian branch. Ronson was Cumbrian through and through, and his dialect was the giveaway; he was king of the vernacular. Although Graham had spoken to Ronson many times, he sometimes failed to understand a single word. Despite this, he was left in no doubt that the economy of this little town would collapse without Ronson and his tiny firm. Ronson disguised his lack of formal qualifications with bluster and the self absorption of falling back on his long history of funeral directing, as if it were an academic progress in itself. He was full of the self importance and the confidence of one who has faithfully time served the same community. His confidence knew no bounds and the crack was that he had walked into the local hospital mortuary, collected a body from the fridge and disappeared back to his premises without a bye nor leave to anyone. The missing corpse had caused mayhem for the hospital staff. Ronson was cautioned but he brushed this off with impunity.

A colleague in the room pointed out Brian, the manager of Flynn's, a family firm in Carlisle. When the founder was alive, the firm was dominant in Carlisle but, as so often with such family firms, the loss of the founder saw funerals decline. Strange, thought Graham, how a business like funeral directing can be a success based on the personality of the owner. This founding Flynn, in black tails, had the tall elegant look and bearing of a film star, and an arrogance to match his stiff top hat. The widows experienced a misplaced, but not unwelcome sensation, in having this dazzling man fussing around them, and that further puffed him up. The measure of a dominant funeral director was his belief that he could call the tune at all the local cemeteries and crematorium; that he could act as the top dog, as if he owned and managed the entire facility and its staff.

The problem with Ben West was that he would not play the underdog. His impudence was evident soon after he arrived at Carlisle when he telephoned heart-throb Flynn to complain that a number of his funerals had been arriving late at the crematorium and had overrun, delaying all subsequent funerals. Far from accepting this, heart-throb Flynn did what he always did in similar situations, he garnered his facial muscles to display his most disdainful sneer, and flashed it at Ben. Feeling that this facial distortion needed verbal back-up, he accused Ben of being a Southerner with big ideas, and reminded him that since arriving, he had upset every funeral director in the area and that he was not a very pleasant person. Flynn had hit below the belt and set himself up for a fall.

The fall was every funeral directors nightmare. The one that made them wake up in a cold sweat at night, the thought that the body had been Fred all its life, but went out as Mabel! The day that the incident occurred, Flynn's were sending two bodies for cremation. The first arrived at the crematorium in the morning, the service took place and the mourners departed. But, when the cremator operator checked the coffin nameplate it was the name of Flynn's second funeral. Was it the right body in the wrong coffin or the wrong body in the right coffin?

Heart-throb Flynn assured Ben that the right body was in the right coffin, and that it was just the wrong lid. The errant lid was swiftly replaced by Flynn's staff and Fred was cremated, in good faith. The second funeral arrived that afternoon; was there a flicker of guilt when Ben quizzed one of Flynn's staff about the body in the coffin? He certainly thought so.

There was only one answer; the body had to be identified. The Salvation Army officer who took the service stepped forward, the lid was removed and Fred really had become Mabel; he had never seen the person before. Heart-throb Flynn had to eat humble pie and apologise to the two families who had held a service over a stranger. At least, thought Graham, they received the right cremated remains and Flynn had thanked his lucky stars that it was kept out of the papers and not reported to the funeral ombudsman. Flynn will have done what they all did when things went wrong; bought the family off.

It was no surprise that complaints to the ombudsman were so low. It was a stock joke in the business that funeral directors got few complaints from their customers. The reality was their unique advantage; their mistakes were always buried or cremated. The mafia came to mind again.

After a warning letter to Flynn from the council, it was Ben one, Flynn nil, thought Graham. One thing was certain, everybody in the business knew what had happened and there was a shift in the power base. The old hands had told Graham that it wouldn't have happened in the past when each corpse had a bespoke hand made coffin, adorned by many different finishes and fittings. The coffin lid with the name Fred on it simply would not have fitted or looked right if inadvertently placed on Mabel's coffin. The different coffin lids were a quality control in their own right but this had all changed. The manufactured bog standard chipboard coffins had the same finish and uniform sizes. It was now too easy to remove two coffin lids for viewing, put them aside and bingo, the wrong lid goes back onto the coffin.

As Graham dwelt on the misdemeanours of Flynn the founder it effortlessly brought to mind the colourful history of Brian. When working for another funeral director he had become very friendly with the boss's wife. Their illicit union was scheduled with the boss's funerals; in constant radio contact they knew precisely where he was. With this idyllic arrangement, both deftly managed their stiffs for some months, but it was inevitable that the boss would realise that the lovebirds were keeping their hands on each other, and their tabs on him. The crack was that he deliberately went on a funeral, but secretly arranged to drive back to the premises. They say that he actually caught them in the act, and as the story elaborated with the telling, they say they were inside a velvet lined American casket!

The denouement was that Brian was subjected to the firm's disciplinary process at the rudimentary level; he was beaten up and sacked. Being personable and young he was soon employed by another firm. Some thought this odd because his other unprofessional quirk was a hatred of top hats; this icon of funeral directing would be cradled within his right arm and was rarely seen on his head. But Brian said he could always get work because he had an O level, and this made the more cynical funeral directors refer to him as, the professor.

Graham was attending the meeting in the company of his boss Bill Roberts, a stout, red faced man. He was a local JP in his early sixties and owner of the old family firm of Roberts &

Son. Graham knew that Bill really disliked, even hated, Ben West but the reasons for this were not entirely obvious. It seemed to stem as far back as 1984, when Ben was new to Carlisle and wanted to change the crematorium grounds because of complaints from the bereaved that they were bleak. Bill was so annoyed he had challenged Ben and pitched in with a defence of the open lawns; how they had satisfied Carlisle people for decades; how Ben's predecessor had been satisfied with them and what right did he have to change them? With much emphasis and gravitas, he had told him that he would have the grounds looking like a bloody circus! He had put Ben straight and stated that, unlike his predecessor, he was no gentleman. Was this class war? Bill was public school and perhaps he suspected that Ben was a secondary modern upstart.

Graham realised that Bill was an old fart. His funerals had to be Churchillian, Christian and represent the moral fabric of the country. He was all Round Table and moral rectitude. Decent people did not play pop songs at funerals and his body language gave out increasingly negative messages. His funeral numbers had been steadily falling but he was liked by the aged well-to-do, who were reassured by his conservatism. But modern life irked him, his children were not interested in the firm and for years it had been said that he intended to sell the business.

Graham suspected that this clash with Ben was really all about gratuities; it was the elephant in the room. All the old funeral directors, and many of the new, used gratuities to oil the funeral process, to keep people sweet. It was a staple part of the business; how could it be wrong? It was so routine to leave a tip at the crematorium or cemetery after a funeral that if it was forgotten, there would be a telephone call to put it right.

Graham recalled somebody telling him that this custom came from Greek mythology, where a coin was paid to Charon to ferry the body over the river Styx. Perhaps, in Carlisle, the river Styx was the B5299, the road to the crematorium. Others had told him that gratuities were paid because the disposal of bodies was originally a job for untouchables, and that if their palms were not greased they might place a curse. Graham was uncertain whether it was just proof that they were all greedy bastards.

The letter from Ben to all the funeral directors had been a shock, and really upset Bill; all gratuities to council staff were to cease, that it would be gross misconduct and staff would be disciplined. But Graham knew it wasn't just the council putting the finger on backhanders, it was Ben wanting to keep out of the pockets of the funeral directors. The unmentionable had now been mentioned. Graham could see how Bill needed the power of the sweetener, it bought acquiescence, it ensured that minions kowtowed to funeral directors, watched out for them, did not hassle about late forms and little errors. How dare Ben challenge such an established practice; he was stepping way over the line.

Graham was pulled back to the present when Bill pointed out Roger Riley. He was always referred to as the people's funeral director because his funerals tended to be working class. The older hands called him the barrow boy. Rumour had it that he was doing more than three hundred funerals a year but then he did have a unique advantage when dealing with the bereaved; he could cry on cue. As a widow looked down upon the face of her late husband, he would stream tears; at the funeral service he would stream tears; at the handing over of the funeral bill he would stream tears, but at the bank, he was all smiles. With his funeral numbers going up every year, he was fair play for the crack. They sneered at his small end of terrace premises; the sitting room was reception, the dining room the Chapel of Repose, the kitchen the body store. Success bred its own problems, as with so little space, coffins were routinely piled one on top of another. The crack was that when a widow arrived unannounced to see her husband, all hell broke loose in the back room if his body was at the bottom of the pile. They could easily be heard through the thin walls so coffins were shuffled without speaking, scraping or bumping, and the correct one transferred to the Chapel of Repose. The coffin lid was removed and the staff metamorphosed instantly into calm serenity as the widow entered. If she ever wondered why her late husband's face was flushed, it was perhaps because, minutes earlier, he was under two other women for the first and only time in his life!

Even by funeral director standards, Roger was considered parsimonious. He paid poorly and by the coffin lift, and his all-male bearers were part-time and the oldest ever seen. They looked as if they had difficulty picking themselves up, let alone a coffin. Roger would insist that his four, and more often than not, six bearers, had to stand in full view and side by side as the hearse approached and stopped. The bearers, neatly dressed in black suits had to be seen by the mourners in the following limousines. Roger considered this a measure of a quality service; that people could see what they got for their money. In fact, what everybody saw was a row of old men with their hands neatly cupped over their testicles. This might seem appropriate for virile young footballers anticipating a large leather ball smacking into their bits but with these old men it just looked ridiculous. It had an unfortunate effect; an inappropriate smile at a funeral.

The crack noted that Roger's relationship with Ben had a touch of ambivalence about it. Whilst seemingly opposed to Ben's changes, he was often seen chatting to him at funerals, or whilst delivering forms to his offices. If he seemed comfortable with Ben then it might have been because he did him a great favour; Ben had got him the sack from his previous funeral directing job.

Roger had the habit of cutting corners where the law was concerned because he knew the law was an ass. On this particular occasion he had put in cremation forms in the name of 'Swindells', but the widow had signed as 'Swindles'. It didn't call for a brain surgeon to realise that somebody other than the widow had signed them; somebody too lazy to visit her. In fact, widow Swindles had never seen the forms let alone signed them, so Ben wings off a warning letter to the firm. A few days later Roger was sacked. Rumours abounded that Ben did Roger's bosses a favour. The irony was that Roger cocked a snook by promptly opening his own funeral directing business and the rest was history.

Graham and the BALU members were finally called to order and sat randomly around the room. He could see that there were a number of smaller funeral directors present, who watched and listened, but rarely participated. Some said that they didn't like the pettiness and flak at the meetings. Graham vaguely knew Willy Bland, a funeral director with two sidelines, one as a builder and one as a salesman for Easysleep beds, manufactured at a local factory. Willy didn't realise that this was vertical integration but he was canny. As most people die in bed, with a relaxation of orifices, it often renders the bed in need of replacement. Graham wondered whether he took a direct approach and said to the widow, "Now you are sleeping on your own, do you need a single bed?" Graham knew that Willy lacked the guile of the big firms; he broke a taboo in bragging about his earnings. He told cemetery staff, key players in the grapevine, that funerals were easy money. He reckoned he spent about two hundred pounds on a funeral, and charged five hundred pounds, so there was a handsome profit. He boasted, "One funeral a week and I am ticking over; two funerals and I'm in profit; three and I can spend all my time on the golf course." It was careless talk to gravediggers who did the hard manual work on low wages.

Graham had his boss on his left, and Peter Porter, another small funeral director, on his right. Peter had a strange little quirk. He would load his pockets with small coins, then, whilst on a funeral would constantly fondle them; lifting them, turning them, dropping them. This rhythmic jingling punctuated the quiet periods between prayers and during reflective moments. Some might have imagined it was heavenly tinkling but to those who knew him it was just a bloody irritating habit.

Opposite was Jack Dudson, another small player. His quirk was funny rather than irritating. When he arrived at a cemetery for a burial service, he would always ask the staff if they had the soil ready for when the vicar says, 'ashes to ashes, dust to dust,' and a sprinkling of soil is scattered on the coffin. Invariably, this person has the soil ready, so Jack turns aside, empties a mass of damp sticky soil out of his suit pocket and finishes with, 'from my garden, just in case.'

To start the meeting, Ronson stood up, which was

unusual, and duly put on his funereal face. He had spoken to the BALU head office in London about all the national publicity for the natural burial scheme in Carlisle. They were worried because if it succeeded, its effect on the death industry could be massive. He reminded members that the Cumbria Branch had always had a low profile, but now they were on the front line. It was that Daily Telegraph article that did it.

Yes, it certainly was, thought Graham. Charles Clover, their environmental writer had called the article 'A New Way of Death'. What had really upset everyone was the suggestion by Ben that existing funerals didn't meet people's needs. Charles Clover even said that he was not alone in thinking this.

Ronson continued by saying that their policy of painting Ben as an isolated green weirdo was not working. He suggested that at least Clover had called him a neo-pagan, which must be bad! The trouble was, head office considered that the Cumbria branch had lost its grip. They had reminded him that no other branch had allowed such a situation to develop. Too much information was getting out there and they were not in control.

Ronson said there had also been stuff on the radio, including Radio Cumbria, so at least ten people had heard it. But then the BBC Today programme had covered it and out it went, on the World Service. Graham could see that for Ronson, it was not just undermining the Cumbrian Branch of BALU, it was a personal affront. For Graham it just brought to mind the Carlisle United fans chanting, 'we are the Dumbrians!'

Ronson hardly drew breath, "The problem is, it's not just this natural burial. This green leaflet here tells people what we should be telling them, and more. He actually says that bodies don't have to be embalmed and that our coffins are polluting. He even tells them that they can do a funeral without a funeral director, and that they will sell them a coffin, a bloody cardboard one. It's got to stop!"

BALU saw their members as the experts and the only ones who could judge what people really needed. They were convinced that too much raw information would confuse and upset the bereaved; that they can be told too much. A DIY funeral and details of embalming; how insensitive can it get? The mood in the room was sombre.

Graham was nonplussed. Surely, there can't be many people out there who want to be buried in a cardboard coffin, in a field, with an oak tree on top? Why not leave them to it? Who was he to say no? But he could see that there were wider issues so perhaps they were right to worry. Some of them in the room now sold stone memorials. The idea that an oak tree could replace an expensive slab of Chinese granite really upset them. He could see faces in the room calculating the hundreds of pounds of lost profit if memorials were deemed unnecessary, let alone embalming and chipboard coffins. The bigger players were even more worried; they talked of the death care industry, proof that they had adopted the American way of death. Death could not be seen as a natural event. It required experts, intervention, chemicals, apparatus and big memorials.

By this time Ben had arrived for the meeting. Graham settled back into his chair thinking this could get interesting; he's either brave or so stupid that he's unaware of the mayhem he's causing. But Ben didn't appear intimidated as he explained about the natural burials, using his large hands to emphasise points, as if he was in the pulpit. Fifty graves had been sold in advance but not a single funeral had taken place. Now some hesitation showed; some of the grave purchasers wanted cardboard coffins but their enquiries to funeral directors had drawn a blank. He finished by pointing out that not a single funeral director had shown any interest in the natural burial scheme; was there a problem?

Ronson had the first question ready; tell us about these cardboard coffins as he had never seen one? Ben miscalculated, he accepted the question at face value and innocently explained who made them, that they were flat-pack, and rather like a big shoe box. Ronson got what he wanted, laughter. The man was clearly delusional. Confidence rose and the mood lightened. Ronson sensed the advantage and suggested Ben just wanted a foot in the door of funeral directing; he wanted to sell these cardboard coffins and undermine their profession. Before Ben could answer, a voice shouted out that Ben wanted to destroy their livelihood. The heat was rising and amongst the jibes and mutterings, another voice clearly said that people who wanted these shoeboxes and natural burial were weirdoes.

Graham wondered if all BALU meetings were as entertaining as this, but then his attention was diverted. Bill, next to him, was snorting and spluttering and when he looked round, he was taken aback; he had never seen him in such a rage. He stood up to his full height, eyeballed Ben and exploded, "I am violently opposed to these ideas. You just want to bring fucking Pakis to Carlisle for burial!"

The room was stunned into silence! This was racist and had nothing to do with Ben's proposals. "There is no call for language like that," was Ronson's quick response, and he gestured to have Bill hustled out of the room. Everyone knew the meeting was over. What an embarrassment! The man is a JP, thought Graham, and everyone knew this. He had to keep these thoughts to himself, as he sat silently next to Bill on the long drive back home.

CHAPTER TWO

Be Still My Love

Graham often enjoyed funerals. Little old ladies would make the arrangements with him, mainly because it was men, the weaker sex in mortality statistics, who expired first. Women were the survivors. Men rarely went to the doctors and spent their last years deluded into thinking the frail woman, the creaking gate, would fall apart in their absence. In fact, he recognised that many of the widows found a new freedom from a lifetime of caring and cooking. Liberties and out of character indulgencies would occur and the widows, as guilty survivors, would justify these by saying, 'It's what he would have wanted.' Graham had some doubt that the old man would have wanted, or expected, them to be indulging in round the world cruises with P & O, but he saw the funny side of it. There was none of the predatory male about Graham. He was young, with that look of innocence that was in need of mothering; the perfect funeral director material for appealing to the widow. Unfortunately, it was not always gentle widows. The funeral they had just booked made him uneasy. In this instance, he was dealing with a man; a man with a reputation, and he sensed that his delicate attributes were a positive disadvantage.

Graham had lived in a number of small rural towns and he knew the score. There is always a seedy area, where an address can strike fear. In Carlisle the Raffles Estate was a brand; the good people tainted by the bad. When he warned Ben West of the impending funeral, Ben had told him that in Shrewsbury, where he'd schooled, there were similar areas. People from these enclaves lived with violence, and it spilled out into funerals and often came through the generations, 'there was bad blood between them'. They were the ones who fought in pubs; who everyone dreaded meeting on the last bus home. None of this was new and in the past there had been laws to stop 'brawling at funerals'. The word brawl leapt out at him as he looked at the name of the funeral applicant.

It was Rollo, burly and brutal; a man who had enlivened the local newspapers for decades. He was noted for his direct action, his disinclination to verbal resolution, and his liking for a pint, or ten. One of his notorious deeds arose after a dog crapped in his garden. He immediately killed it and posted the severed paws through the owner's letter box. You paused for thought before you got involved with Rollo, though Graham.

Rollo's common law partner Doreen rivalled his column inches with her turn as a well known drug addict and drunk. Occasionally she put in some variation as a punched and bruised partner. In her early forties, and laced with drink and drugs, she died miserably in a public toilet; a blessed relief thought many.

It was with some relief that Graham found Rollo to be amenable and intent on doing right by his missus. It took four days for the police to complete a report and for the coroner to release her body for the cremation. To do right for Doreen, Graham and his colleagues carefully masked the facial damage. To be right for Rollo, Doreen had to come home, so the coffin, light and easy to carry, was placed on trestles in the dining room.

Early the next day a man telephoned the Carlisle Photographic Studio and asked if someone could come round that morning to photograph him and the missus. A young lady was dispatched with her camera, finds the house, meets a bulky but friendly man, and is ushered into the lounge. As she prepares her camera, the husband is gently and silently arranging his beloved in an armchair. The photographer turns, pauses and exclaims, "Your wife doesn't look too well". Her sentence was truncated as the words transformed into a scream as she ran out. It was some time before she regained her composure and longer still before she realised that she had added a significant skill to her CV, 'experienced in still life!'

Graham, unaware of the photo session, arrived at the house to collect Doreen expecting Rollo to be ready; all was quiet. He knocked the door but there was no response. Concerned, he called through the letter box and Rollo answered, "Fuck off, we're not coming!" Graham realised that some furniture was behind the door; Rollo had barricaded himself in the house. A short discussion through the letterbox was punctuated by expletives and Graham reached a conclusion; the funeral was going to be late! The police were summoned and they immediately send the BBMT unit, locally known as the brutal bastard mediation team. Graham also phoned Ben to cancel the cremation service; the body is unavoidably detained!

The police have a dilemma! In the eyes of the law, Rollo, as her common law husband, was entitled to possession of her body; there was no misdemeanour. The body was not decomposing or a threat to public health, whatever that might be, so still there was no misdemeanour. The immediate threat, the police knew, was not to public health but to them. In the

21

circumstances, storming the house to recover the body of a deceased, alcoholic drug taker seemed heavy handed. Neither did it seem appropriate to bring in the dog team! They decided that mediation was the only answer, especially as it did not need a large vocabulary. Their plea was that poor Doreen needed a proper funeral service and laying to rest, and with this logic, Rollo finally allowed two policemen inside.

The police quickly turned into counsellors. They sensed that Rollo, like all bullies, was now deeply remorseful. He described how he had removed her body from the coffin and there was her throat, cut side to side. Why hadn't they done their job properly; someone had slashed her? It was no easy matter to convince him that this was part of the postmortem. They praised him for his concern, they gave him time and patience and it was as if he was appeased by Doreen being given so much time and attention. He relented and finally allowed Graham to collect her body.

Graham now experienced a new fear. If Rollo went looking for Doreen then he is the innocent dog on the lawn! Ben comes to his aid, Doreen is secreted in a remote chapel and the service rearranged for the following morning. A low key police presence is promised; an entire squad rolls up! The police were secreted and with only Rollo, Graham and the vicar at the funeral, it passed without incident. Doreen was finally at peace.

CHAPTER THREE

Snitch at the WI

I wish they'd stick to jam and Jerusalem, thought Marjorie, and stayed away from death. The thought arose because the apologies for absence from the chairwoman were higher than usual. The subject was challenging, she said, with a look and tone that implied they were wimps and traitors to female emancipation. I'd be absent too, thought Marjorie, if our Roger hadn't asked me to report back on this talk of Ben West's. She didn't question Roger very much, but she was conscious that Ben had really upset him. She chatted to a few of the other women and it was apparent some had already heard him speak before, and it was said that one of the women had even arranged a DIY funeral. He obviously had some groupies so she was guarded in her comments. He didn't look much either, just the usual council sort she expected. Once he got going, she wrote furiously in her little notebook and then returned home.

When Roger phoned later and said he would call the following morning, she realised how important her comments were to him. When he arrived the next day, she said, "Roger, you didn't warn me that he liked flattering the ladies though it cut no ice with me." He laughed at this, as she mashed the tea. As they chatted, she quickly sensed that he wanted to know it all, from the very beginning, and not just the bits about funeral directors. "He's a bit full of 'imself, likes the sound of his own voice, I'd say. He was cracking jokes before you could say owt, about how he enjoyed the opportunity to talk to older audiences, and that sort o' thing. Said that the most dangerous person was the doctor because they'd all seen one just before they died!" Roger smiled and told her that Ben always did this to ease in his subject, it's just his way.

"Well he got into them baby-boomers and how much longer people were living now, and then got in a dig at funeral directors." "How did he do that," asked Roger. "He was saying that the good news about living longer is that it gives you more time to save up for your funeral." She saw Roger smile but carried on, "Then he did his flattering bit by saying how women were the survivors, they were stronger and lived longer than men, which was why women arranged 70% of funerals. It was men wot annoyed him when they said things like stick me in a black plastic bag and throw me over a wall." Marjorie paused as if contemplating this point, then poured a second cup of tea.

"He then told us how the word bereaved had come from them Scots reiving our sheep and cattle over the border, that you were be-reived when you lost som'at. He annoyed me, you know, he's a cocky bugger." She looked at Roger, conscious that he knew she was married to an Elliot, one of the border reiver families. "He got a bit more serious after that and said it didn't matter how much was spent on the funeral an' memorials an' that because the modern funeral just reinforced loss." Roger asked, "What did he mean by that?" "I think he was saying you funeral directors are all into black, the tops hats and all that stuff."

"He had a go at cremation saying it caused pollution and

wasted loads of gas. I think he said it spread embalming fluid across the skies. He had a go at you again because he said that funeral directors liked cremation because it was quick, and they could do more funerals in a day." She stopped and said, "Do you think this is true Roger, this pollution thing?" He suspected that she was bothered because she had arranged her mother's cremation with him a year earlier. "No, I don't think it's true because well over 70% of people are cremated; all those people can't be wrong, can they?"

"He then got into this natural burial thing, as you warned me. About how it changed everything because if you cremated you destroyed the body, this way you used the body to make trees an' butterflies and things. Made the world a better place, he seemed to think. Although he'd only done a few of these funerals, he said it seemed to change the way people wanted to do them. Not all black, but casual like, even T-shirts at one. He went on about cardboard coffins and embalming and it all sounded very odd." Roger nodded in agreement and said the idea was stupid.

Marjorie looked at her notes, "Then he said a lot about funeral directing. First there was a bit of a sop about what a good job some of you do, and that there are a lot of caring people. Then he said the big firms were taking over by hiding under old family names, how the chipboard coffins and plastic handles were a cheat because they looked like real wood and brass. He mentioned what I think he called a funeral package, which he said stopped people having just the bits of funerals they wanted."

Roger asked her how the members reacted to Ben's talk and she said that they asked lots of questions, and funeral bills worried a few. He asked whether there seemed to be any support for natural burial, but Marjorie didn't like to say. He then asked whether anybody mentioned DIY funerals and she told him that one woman had jumped up and told everyone about her dad's funeral. She'd done it herself, helped by Ben's staff. This was because when her mother had died, two young men from the funeral directors sent her out of the bedroom when they collected her mother's body, so she couldn't see what they were up to. She had felt really bad that she had allowed them to take over. It was because of this, that she would never go to a funeral director again.

Marjorie could see that Roger was more annoyed now. He pushed her on whether Ben had said any more but she seemed to have exhausted her notes; there was no more. Roger asked how she felt about his talk and she said she was irritated by him. He was telling Cumbrians how to do their funerals and it wasn't right. Roger finally asked whether he said they were charging too much. Marjorie was confused, "He didn't say that outright but he felt that you all made it complicated and confusing so that people didn't know how much it would all cost. There doesn't seem to be any love lost between him and you funeral directors, that's for sure." Roger kissed his aunt goodbye and left as a man in no doubt; Ben had said that funeral directing was a rip-off!

CHAPTER FOUR

Separate Ways

Graham kept an ear to the ground after the big BALU meeting because everybody had been dumbfounded. It was not just the inquisition on Ben or natural burial that was really the issue, they knew there was more to come on that. It was that the relationship had taken a new turn, thought Graham, BALU and Ben now had no choice; each was on their own path.

The violent outburst from Bill had unsettled every BALU member. The last person they had wanted to witness what happened, was Ben. It wasn't what was expected from a JP, who might be sitting on the bench the following day. What if the accused was a Pakistani? What made Bill think that they would want to come to Carlisle for a cardboard coffin and a natural burial? A new type of asylum seeker, that's for sure! It was absurd. One thing was certain; any foreigner who came before him would be dispensed rough justice. The only fairness, thought Graham, was that Bill would deal with an offcomer with the same degree of justice.

✝

Roger Riley had almost enjoyed the meeting. He had no time for the old stuffed shirts like Bill. Seeing him lose face was a pleasure in itself but he returned to the present; he was not having a good day. He needed to take the CD player with him that morning to a graveside service. His wife had placed it on the drive so that he could not miss it. He didn't; he drove straight over it. A smaller car might have baulked, but the big limo just rolled over and crushed it quite flat, CD and all. The widow had requested the track 'Give me a man after midnight' and now his staff were urgently trying to find another copy at local music shops.

At least his cremation service had no last minute panic. He was master of ceremonies and was doing what he enjoyed most; people watching. The male mourners were from villages around Carlisle and, true to tradition, they were colour coded. Various shades of brown suits had always been the haute couture of Cumbrian farmers. Blobs of cow shit and sheep shit disappeared when set against this colour so there was a rural logic. Forced by the occasion, these bucolic people had swapped working clothes for formal attire; not a man looked at ease in his suit. Roger thought that there must be a market for a modern smock for these people to wear at funerals. What really irritated him, though, was their tardy reluctance to move forward into the chapel. They had to be herded, like sheep, to get them inside the chapel doors. Then, inside and just like bloody sheep, they flocked into the rear pews, elbowing each other rather than simply moving forward to empty seats. Roger would actually stand in the aisle and implore them to come to the front. Even then, with the back rows full they would jostle to stand at the back shoulder to shoulder. He knew a psychologist could spend a lifetime studying these people, but it was beyond him. So, in his top hat and tails, unfazed, he would turn and bow to the vicar as if to say, the sheep are penned and the service can begin.

Roger returned to the office for a sandwich after the service, to find a police detective waiting to see him and clutching a small package. He explained that in the package, which was found on a doorstep, was a human finger, with no fingernail. "Oh", said Roger, "It was handed in, was it?" The policeman did not find this amusing.

The detective appeared grave, as if the contents of the package might shock him. As if an amputated finger, thought Roger, could shock a man who has scraped human flesh off the highway. Roger peered at the finger but was unimpressed by the three inch digit. The detective was adamant; there was a fingerless corpse somewhere in Carlisle. He had checked the mortuary for missing digits, and no bodies had been dug up at the local cemeteries and churchyards. He now intended visiting every funeral director in the area. He had, thought Roger, got to put the finger on somebody!

He wanted to tell the detective that he was barking up the wrong tree. To think that Roger or any other funeral director could miss a finger. He knew it wasn't like a birth, where the midwife counted all the fingers and toes, but they weren't stupid, or blind. Roger retracted that thought when he recalled a funeral director in London, who took a coffin to a local crematorium. It was obvious to the staff that it was too light; there was no body inside! The funeral director immediately blamed his new team. The crematorium manager countered that surely they had checked the identity when they put the lid on the coffin. "Good God!" he said, "We haven't got time to check there's a body in every bloody coffin!"

Roger wished that he had looked more closely at the finger

when, after eight days of investigations, it was realised that it was a hoax. It was a pig's tail carefully cut to look like a human finger. A practical joker, they decided, but Roger was never able to eat bacon again without a flicker of a smile.

As Roger finished his sandwich he pondered; what was Ben going to do next? Clearly, Ben went to the BALU meeting to ask for their support but what happened had closed everything down. Neither the members nor Ronson seemed sure what to do. Roger was confident that did not include him. He was going to keep his finger on the pulse, Ben's pulse. Perhaps, he and Ben would just have to go their own separate ways. The rest of them can either catch up or go down.

His first impulse on next meeting Ben had been to make an outright apology over Bill's outburst but it seemed ridiculous; nobody was hurt and anyway, it wasn't his responsibility. His business brain then dictated that he should sympathise with Ben so there were a few brief platitudes. Ben seemed unconcerned and there was no opportunity to say more because they were on a funeral. He mulled over the issues and some weeks later made an appointment to see Ben because the natural burial enquiries were increasing; how should he respond?

He found Ben upbeat because there had recently been three natural burials. Roger already knew this, because the local papers, who were following it closely, had reported them as the first 'green funerals' in the world. He didn't have to ask who the funeral directors were because the crack told him they were all DIY funerals; he was there to find out all about them.

One had been from the Bahai faith, people with an ethos which required a simple and low cost funeral, then a bee keeper and environmentalist, and the third, somebody who just wanted a cheap funeral. He suspected the funerals would be different so asked how they dressed. The Bahais' had, as he expected, dressed soberly but the other families, wanting the funerals to be celebrations of a life, had requested any colour other than black.

Roger then commented that these people might want to get away from traditional funerals but this experience suggested that the natural burial graves were just for cheapskates. But, Ben was ready, and surprised him by saying how many graves were being pre-purchased, many by well-to-do people. It was their way of supporting the idea whilst they were alive. They had every intention of using a funeral director and were certainly not cheapskates. Even so, Roger knew that because they were having a natural burial, they would avoid a chipboard coffin and embalming. He had hinted that funeral directors might refuse such funerals but Ben was confident; with enough people power, they would have no choice.

Roger left Ben's office and decided now was the time to have a look at the natural burial plot. He walked through the Victorian gate and looked up the grand drive, lined by an avenue of towering, clipped, yew trees. As he walked he looked into beautiful glades full of graves and memorials on mossy grass. He saw nothing gloomy or morbid as other people might; it was his repository of funerals. Over the years he had arranged a burial or two on almost every plot. An epitaph here or there reincarnated into people; he was confident he could recall every family who ever arranged a funeral with him. His recall was instant; they were all vibrant and alive in his mind. That was the one, who told him the shocking titbit he really didn't want to know. With others, he

31

recalled the banal gossip about who was not married to whom, their physical traits, the often bizarre and odd things that slip out during the intimacy that is a funeral arrangement. There, was the grave of the young spoiled son, crushed to death in the fast car his doting mother bought him; she now sleepless with guilt. There, was Jim Granger's grave, a tightwad who deprived his wife of everything, she now living the life of Riley, his namesake. There, the recluse, whose house was filled ceiling high with old newspapers; the rats nesting inside. And that grave was the spontaneous homily, the time when an ex-wife shouted out during a quiet part of the funeral service, "You twat, I hope you fucking pay for leaving me!" Funerals expose warts and all, like nothing else, thought Roger.

He turned left to the Gothic chapel. Passing the huge owl carved into a fifteen foot stump of an old tree trunk, a mother with a young child exclaimed that she could not walk through the cemetery without her daughter saying hello to Barny. The little girl called it the biggest owl in the world. He walked on, crossing Fairy Beck via the footbridge. On reaching the war plot he stopped and read a relatively new inscription of a woman's name and the years 1926 – 1993; Violet, a Christian name which appealed to new mothers in the 1920's. The curt inscription belied the sadness of her story; a woman widowed with two children after an emaciated Chindit arrived home in 1945 too ill to survive. He knew he had just walked through Carlisle's history, but who really cared now?

He noticed pot mums everywhere, lovingly placed one to a grave, this floral homage now nature's dessert. The rabbits adored these Chrysanthemum flowers, and nipped them off. Their teeth mimicked a pair of shears, neat and precise, perfectly level. Here and at cemeteries all over the country people blamed careless cemetery staff; unwilling to accept cuddly bunnies as the culprits.

He stopped at the entrance to the natural burial plot, the past, his past, bounced into the present. A woman waved to attract his attention and said, "I shouldn't be surprised to see a funeral director in a cemetery." They greeted each other warmly because Roger had arranged her mother's funeral many years earlier. He felt comfortable, aware she treated him with respect, an intimacy that a car salesman can only dream of, and he asked, "What brings you here?" "My sister wanted to see the natural burial plot because she's bought her grave today." He could not ignore the ease in which she said this, and the way this ease clashed with his BALU experience. "Sis," she called to a woman just inside the plot, "Tell Roger how you were going to be buried in your back garden."

"Well, I was," she said. "I live in Dumfries and I tried for ages to find out how to be buried in my back garden under a tree. The environmental health people were okay but thank goodness they put me on to Mr. West. He knew the law, confirmed I could do it but made me realise that a body in the garden would be a bit of a turn-off for buyers, and greatly reduce the value of my house. I didn't know that if I was buried in the garden then the new owner could dig me up and move me to a cemetery. Well, there was no way I wanted that to happen." Roger listened intently, "Did he ask you why you wanted to do this?" "Yes, I told him I'd been in contact with the Natural Death Centre in London. Told them I'm not going to be burnt and cause more pollution, nor am I going in one of those awful lawn graves." Roger showed surprise at this, "What's wrong with the lawn graves?" "Well, let's face it,

33

they are boring rows of headstones and all that mowing is hardly environmental." Roger was shocked that this ordinary woman had such thoughts, but he did not say so. "I said the same to Mr. West, but then I reminded him that I'm single so I have nobody to care for the grave after I'm gone. What's the point of a gravestone with nobody to visit, it will just look abandoned and uncared for? Then he asked if it would solve my problem if he provided some sort of tree grave, one that nature would care for." Her sister butted in, "See Roger, my sister started this natural burial, it's all her doing."

The three of them walked into the plot, a portion of field and unimpressive. The sister asked him to follow and after a short walk, drew up in front of an aluminium number on the ground. "This is it, my final resting place. A small oak tree will go on top and some bluebells." He wanted to say that the plot lacked trees, but she sensed his negativity. "This is how it all starts, our bodies feed an oak tree and the new wood will be really good for the environment, you know. And, it will make the world a better place." He probed on the kind of funeral she planned to have and was surprised when she said that she was going to have just an ordinary funeral. He was uncertain what she meant and teased it out, and to her it was a hearse and limo, everybody in black and her vicar taking the service. She saw this as ordinary, but would want a cardboard coffin and definitely no embalming. There was a complete innocence in her desire with no sense of any obstacles in her way. From her comments, it was also obvious that they were going to look to him when the time came to arrange the funeral; they anticipated that he, Roger Riley, would look after them.

Roger said farewell to the women, and walked back to the gate. He knew he had a dilemma; people were going green.

Neither he nor any of the other funeral directors had yet arranged a green funeral, but it was just a matter of time. Quietly, ordinary people were now pre-purchasing the graves; there were funerals to be gained. He could sense the change because he had pre-arranged hundreds of funerals over the years but they were just a means to an end, just disposing of a body; they didn't invest the decision with the same feeling and emotion. Not twelve months ago he had felt that burial was finished; now it was all the talk. The few burials he had done had been those who feared burning, wanted to go in an existing grave or for religious reasons. This was different. What did she say? Good for the environment; make the world a better place. Here was a woman from tiny Dumfries telling him that his coffins pollute and bodies nurture trees. Next thing, she will be quoting Ben about transporting granite memorials from China. He realised that these people no longer wore anoraks. In future, he would have to avoid calling them greens and weirdoes.

†

Bill Roberts the JP, Paki basher, reflected upon what he had said at the BALU meeting. He justified it by blaming Ben for upsetting everybody. He felt depressed at the fuss he had caused but he was going to get out of funerals anyway, so why care? It was getting around that he was going to sell out. He felt out of kilter with BALU, conscious he was always whinging. He sensed his own negativity whenever he spoke, so they must have noticed. He was always harping back to when people did as they were told; it was a Christian country and they should have a Christian funeral. In the past it was left to him to arrange a vicar, even a rota vicar and nobody took much interest in what was said or what hymns were sung. Now, they even demanded that he should ask the vicar to soften down the religious content. It was all so depressing.

One family had insisted that because they were paying the vicar a hefty fee, they could and would, play a raunchy pop song by Suzi Quattro. He didn't want to get involved but found himself delicately mediating between both parties. Then, there were these new poems about the deceased not really being dead, just hiding in the next room. Some vicars hated all this stuff so he was constantly put in a difficult position. They knew that the old Bill would have refused, so they saw him as the problem, and not the families. Bill sighed nostalgically for the time when only the rich and well-to-do made demands over funerals. Now, even council tenants off the Raffles Estate treated him as an equal, and based their funerals on East Enders. Only weeks before, a young family of a lorry driver who had died had wanted him to be referred to by his driver's CB tag – beaverbanger! He cringed at the memory.

He was resigned to getting out. He had noticed in the articles in the funeral director's journals that there were fewer and fewer in his camp; the newer funeral directors accepted these changes; they knew no different. The latest issue was whether it was good for children to attend funerals. It was nuts! In the past nobody wanted children at funerals but now the experts said that if they did not go they would develop a phobia about death. You would not think they were talking about kids who sat at a computer for hours on end and personally decapitated, shot, stabbed, drove over and cut-up with a power saw, hundreds of cyber people – that was when they were not looking at porn. So now the parents pontificate for days over whether little Jonny should be told about the death, let alone see the body or attend the funeral. They often asked Bill for his views but, with negative vibes, he would say that the decision must be theirs. What did he know; he never used a computer and still had a picture of the Queen in his hall.

CHAPTER FIVE

Poodle in Paradise

Graham was not surprised to read about companions' graves in Ben's letter because the BALU members had already discussed it. They had pooh-poohed it, as he anticipated, but he was annoyed with himself, because he had failed to voice support for the scheme. He felt sure that there were others at the meeting who liked the idea, but if so, they also remained mute. It was a given that all proposals from Ben were to be rejected. Ben was, after all, asking for their opinion prior to applying for planning permission. Was a grave for pet lovers so shocking? Are we not a nation of pet lovers? He knew that it would be appealing to many people to have their grave next to a half grave for their pets. There was something comforting about having the memorial between the two graves; the human and pet names united in death as in life. He knew it was right for him, and he represented a mass of people out there. He knew that it was mostly dogs Ben was really talking about; it was dogs that had the most emotional attachment. Graham had always thought that dogs had evolved inappropriately; they lived too short a life. Owners fretted about what they had done with dead pets, some buried in the garden, some incinerated but in bulk along with other animals. The companions' idea would have enabled all their pets to go into the one grave, waiting for their doting owner to join them; walkies, together, forever!

Graham was passionate on this issue. It arose so often when arranging the funerals of old people who lived alone; what to do with their orphaned pet? They were often put down because they pined, or were just too old to re-home. At least this way they could all end up together, but BALU didn't care a toss about pets even though the members experienced the same problems as he did. Pets were more valued than humans by some people, they could certainly be more trustworthy and faithful.

Some of the BALU members had justified their opposition by saying that the clergy might not like it, but, thought Graham, there are some very strange ministers out there. He reflected on one minister who, accompanied by sweeping arm movements to encapsulate the entire cemetery, would say, "And one day, dear friends, all the dead shall rise up out of this ground…" Graham could imagine the cemetery gridlocked with the once dead, but there was a serious question; why aren't these people in paradise? It was the word paradise that bemused him. Before he was into funerals he had never given the word a second thought, but now it arose daily and could not be ignored. Those uttering the word so randomly, the ministers, people he respected when he knew little about them, had, through familiarity, often become bigoted and uncharitable. These were the people who stated with certainty that dogs have no souls; they cannot go to paradise.

Despite his annoyance, he did have some sympathy with the ministers. Having lost most of their purpose in society, the funeral was one of their few significant events; the final mediation between people and God. This communion with the hereafter made some ministers over confident to the point of sheer arrogance. He had been shocked at those male ministers who detested women coming into the church. At some funerals they would approach him on the car park and ask him to go into the crematorium building to confirm that a female deacon was not present. They would, thought Graham, rather copulate with the devil than accept a woman as a religious equal. Neither dogs nor women in paradise, it seems!

Graham had no problem with the deaconesses; they had no anti-dog dogma. Neither did he experience the agro when telephoning them to make a funeral arrangement. They did not lecture him that it was their day off. There was none of the stuffiness he found in many of the men, they were not so self absorbed. This was even more evident in the male ministers of the bizarre fringe churches. They would wear slick Savile Row suits, have immaculate hair, and even gold watches and cufflinks. They modelled themselves on the American pastors, those fake ministers subsumed in their own self importance and vanity. He had even been upbraided by one of them for not referring to him as pastor. He was the one who had told his congregation that sex was purely for procreation, and must not be used for pleasure. Obviously, an inappropriate orgasm was a heinous sin and would preclude them from paradise. Graham felt paradise must be very empty, and dull. If carnality and gross, unrestrained habits upset these pastors then dogs were definitely out. One pastor, he recalled, preached that everybody would be much more comfortable in paradise because God would not allow any insects to trouble them. That was true, thought Graham, but only because there would be no dog shit.

Graham had expected humanity and spirituality, but was disappointed. His experiences with funerals had changed him and he had become irreligious. He was also realising that most funeral directors felt the same way. They vicar watched all the time, it was an addiction in the profession. None of them went to church outside their work but it was a business ethic; always appear Christian. And he knew that they never, ever, let themselves be seen as doubters; the word atheist was a term of abuse; it was reserved for the likes of Ben.

Perhaps he would call on Ben and tell him that he thought that companions' graves were a good idea, but he was too late. He heard that Ben had already given up the idea after people with loud voices told him the proposal was insensitive. It was not just the ministers and funeral directors who had registered their opposition. The anti-dog lobby, people who regularly visited the cemetery, made representations to a councillor. The matter was closed.

All this made him recall how in the previous year a group of dog haters had written to the papers about dog shit on graves; that all dogs should be banned from the cemetery. He had watched and listened as Ben fought them off by suggesting that the problem was exaggerated, and that some of the poo was dumped by foxes. Ben supported the local dog walkers because he considered them the eyes and ears of the cemetery and felt their presence made other grave visitors feel safer. The conflict ended suddenly when the main pooch hater, an elderly widower, died. The dissent was buried, so to speak. This brought to Graham's mind the funeral of a ninety year old widow. Her daughter had asked if her late mother's dog, a poor old thing, which now had to be put down, could go in the grave with her. The dog's body could not go in the grave but Ben suggested that if she had the dog cremated at the pet crematorium, Paws for Pets, the ashes could go on the coffin. He knew that it was not unusual for people to slip pet's cremated remains into coffins, often with the blessing of their funeral director, so he ignored it. Graham recalled the woman's coffin descending into the grave and sitting on her nameplate was a tiny casket inscribed, 'Billy'. Everyone went away happy.

Graham thought back to his GCSE in humanities. A French philosopher wrote about playing with his cat; was he playing with the cat or was the cat playing with him? The suggestion that a cat could think had so upset the Catholic Church that they banned his writings. Little had changed in 200 years. He broke off musing as he arrived home and opened his front door. A loving female, trusting and uncomplicated, was in the hall to greet him, a bundle of quivering excitement; it was Sherry, his black poodle.

CHAPTER SIX

Coffin on the Rack

"I tell you, the coffin was on the roof rack!" Roger was giving Ronson the crack. Ronson said, "You must be wrong; nobody in their right mind would do that." "But they did," said Roger, "The cardboard coffin was inside a large cardboard box, but it still looked like a coffin." "Surely to God they didn't bring the body back on the roof rack?" As Ronson said this, for a fraction of a second he wondered whether Roger's response would suggest just that, but no, it was inside the car, a Reliant Robin, just like Del Boy's. They had to remove the passenger seat and prop the coffin, with dad inside, on the dashboard. "This is what happens when there's no control, we have to do something," said Ronson, "They could've hired a van, so why use a tiny three wheeler like this?" "I did ask that," said Roger, "It wasn't just the cost, they thought that their dad would have found it all so funny. That he was looking down and laughing with them." "Did anyone see them deliver the coffin to the crem, somebody who might put in a complaint?" said Ronson. "No," said Roger, "Besides, there's nothing odd seeing a coffin delivered to the crematorium." "There is," said Ronson, "If it's propped up on the dashboard of a bloody Reliant Robin."

With this incident, Ronson was reminded that Ben was back in his irritating mode after a quiet few months, so it was no great surprise when he started sending out information leaflets direct to the bereaved family. It was not the usual benign council brochure, full of pretty pictures of memorials and flower beds. This, for the first time, intruded into the intimate relationship between the funeral director and the family. All the BALU members were infuriated. These were their funerals and they had always been the first and only point of contact. He knew that this was Ben's new way; to tell people what they needed to know, before it left the horse's mouth.

It undermined their sales pitch. People, armed with information, could come back and challenge them over what they had said or done; or conveniently forgot to mention. Their cosy, controlled relationship, was disturbed. Funerals had always been a crisis purchase; it was their job to steer them through but now they had an interloper.

Ronson laughed out loud as he read on the leaflets that the crem and cemeteries were to be called City of Carlisle Bereavement Services and Ben, Bereavement Services Manager. The little upstart, thought Ronson. He's taking over our role and we're being demeaned to little more than the supplier of the coffin and hearse.

Despite their anger, it seemed they just had to sit it out. He wondered whether the big companies, with their highfalutin marketing managers and sales blurb, had the answer. He approached Graham on this but he had heard nothing from his senior managers. Yet Ronson knew that Ben's leaflets were being studied, word for word, by every firm. He knew his members and they wanted the quick, easily arranged funeral. Making assumptions was their skill; talking and giving information cost money. But Ronson was adamant; he didn't want to see any letters in the press, so he reminded every member that they should not challenge the leaflets without his say so.

Ronson struggled with all this new fangled marketing and decided to call in Roger, and Graham, who was familiar with these modern ways at his firm. This triumvirate studied the leaflets in detail and came to the conclusion that one of Ben's tactics was to appear virtuous by piggybacking on the environment. He knew, and they knew, that they dare not get into a media battle over the pollution from embalming chemicals or the chipboard in coffins.

Graham said, "It seems to me that too much emphasis is put on the coffin, it mentions biodegradable coffin six times in the main leaflet. He's doing this deliberately because he sees it as one of our weaknesses. He knows that the mark-up on chipboard coffins is high and he's confident that this is the real reason why we won't sell these green coffins." Roger said, "He also makes cremation look polluting; natural burial is all birds and trees and the old choices are portrayed as environmentally bad and unsustainable." Graham then said, "Yes, but that's because he wants people to use the green coffins, whether cardboard or wicker, for cremation, to reduce the pollution. He's not pushing them just for natural burial." Ronson looked resigned; it was stalemate.

Graham then pointed out, "It's not just the environment, there's a mass of social stuff hidden in these leaflets. He's challenging the way we operate, especially where he sees us limiting choice. For instance, he mentions that people have to buy a funeral package, it's all or nothing, that they have to pay for bits they might not need. Then there's the slur when he says that his council unit do not have any commercial incentives; it's this virtue thing again. It's Ben's way of saying our interest is money, and not people."

Roger pointed out, "The leaflets also push the value of a

will, because it makes people consider their funeral. Ben is confident that because this puts an executor into the mix, a person chosen to carry out the wishes of the deceased, they will exert more control. If the deceased wants a simple funeral, he believes that they will resist our influence on other members of the family, the ones who might prefer a good send off, no matter what the cost." Ronson considered this, aware that it was open house for funeral directors when no will was made.

Ronson said, "Surely there's some way we can demand that the council withdraw the leaflets because we consider them scurrilous and misleading?" Even as he said this he knew that both Graham and Roger would be opposed, and they were. Neither wanted to give Ben the satisfaction that he had got at them; they impressed on Ronson that it was just Ben's point of view; nothing he wrote was actually incorrect, it was just below the belt.

Graham summarised, "We mustn't let Ben needle us. We can still get it across that any cutbacks hint at the pauper approach, that they lack dignity. We all know that most people want to do the right thing by the dead; their guilt is reduced if the funeral is conspicuous. We can still get them to follow the American way of death, that love is expressed through spending; it's people who want a good send off, not us." Ronson was impressed by Graham's passion and logic. His company were already adopting the US approach, which they called, 'death care'. It was an approach that suggested cheapskate funerals cost more in the end because the bereaved subsequently needed expensive counselling.

There was no peace for Ronson and he came up in a sweat every time he thought about BALU head office. He had not told them about Ben's leaflets, yet knew that he must send them all the copies. They clashed with everything BALU stood for. The prize for waking him most nights at 4a.m. went to the leaflet about DIY funerals. One of his members had reminded him that the profession had spent a very expensive one hundred years promoting their expertise, and the fact that they were indispensable to the funeral. Yet here was an invitation to people to do their own funeral, collecting the body in a van, caring for it at home, and then taking it to the cemetery or crematorium. The simplicity made it look like the funeral director was superfluous. He knew it was wrong yet the curtness of the text, the bare bones of it, was alluring and seemed somehow doable. He wanted to say that it could not be done, but people were doing it.

Before he contacted BALU he needed a solution, a way forward. He must not look like a man out of his depth. Graham's comments on coffins gave him his lead; the weakness of the DIY funeral was the coffin. People could get hold of those cardboard boxes but most couldn't come to terms with their stark simplicity; they didn't look the part. Few people were aware that they could be covered by a pall or decorated. But, if they wanted a real coffin, hardly anyone could make one and most people had bad vibes about touching them or having one in the house. Also, a coffin had to look like a coffin; it was the funeral icon and had to be a proper and decent receptacle for the dead. Lots of people, especially men, had joked with him about being put in a bin bag and thrown over a wall, but this was just bravado; poor coffins bothered people. Although Ben could provide cardboard coffins, he didn't stock the real McCoy.

Ronson knew how difficult it was to obtain a traditional

coffin because the manufacturers would only sell to bona fide funeral directors. For years BALU had been aware that the easy availability of a coffin would be a threat, and had already lobbied behind the scenes to prevent direct coffin sales. There were strong rumours that B & Q had proposals to put flat-pack coffins on the shelves, but had shied off. The Office of Fair Trading had identified this restrictive practice and after negotiations, was under the impression that funeral directors would now sell coffins direct to the public. He knew it was pure tosh. When approached, few actually said a direct no, but they prevaricated, hinted that it was not usual, and talked up the potential problems of doing it without their help. Many found it embarrassing, wavered and backed off but those who persisted would be sold a basic but expensive coffin.

Ronson was now focussed; it was time to contact BALU head office. They all knew that selling coffins was outside the council's legal powers, but they had the same problem as always; being seen to oppose cast them as mean spirited and protectionist. Head office told Ronson to continue monitoring the situation and keep them updated.

Ronson was soon back in touch after a local coffin manufacturer had mentioned to Brian that Ben had contacted him. Brian immediately realised that he was being sounded out; how would BALU members respond if the manufacturer sold coffins direct to the council? The response had to be immediate, said BALU head office, but they couldn't be seen to be involved, it had to be kept local. Ronson was told to sort it.

Ronson hated such situations because he knew that the Office of Fair Trading had already investigated protectionism by funeral directors; they had come up against a wall of silence.

He wanted to discuss the issue with other members but he decided that the fewer people involved the better. He closed the door and dialled the number he had used many times before. "Morning, Ronson here. I need another five coffins. How is business? Pleased to hear that. We in BALU like to use local firms. It's essential that we look after one another. Isn't that so? We wouldn't want to take our business anywhere else. Ah, that's good; I knew we would feel the same way about it."

Ronson was aware that the manufacturer would detest him and his BALU customers even more now that he had put the squeeze on him over the council sales. It reinforced the fact that they had always had him in a straightjacket. They had held his prices to a bare minimum, constantly warning him that if he increased them then they would go elsewhere. The manufacturer spread it about that he barely made a pound profit on each chipboard coffin and yet they were retailed to the bereaved with at least a one hundred pound mark-up. Ronson slept easy that night. He had sorted it!

The snitches kept Ronson up to date. Ben's coffin order was rejected without explanation, but everyone suspected the reason; the manufacturer had been leaned on. They say Ben threatened to go to the Office of Fair Trading, but he remained coffinless.

†

Coffins were a problem for Brian too, one coffin in particular. It started with a phone call from a widower, "I can see my wife's coffin plate in the grave, which has not been backfilled." Brian mulled over this as he drove to the cemetery to meet Ben's deputy, Thelma, and Mr. Broody. Brian had arranged his late wife's funeral three weeks previously and there had since been numerous niggling phone calls. This had been the latest and had perplexed him because it had never happened before.

When Mr. Broody arrived he walked straight to a grave covered in planks, bent over and showed how he could peer through the gaps and see his wife's coffin. He said he was so perturbed that he dared not move the planks aside to look into the dark depths. Brian and Thelma were immediately puzzled as to why no flowers had been placed by him for over three weeks, which was the usual reason for visits.

Brian then gently pointed out to Mr. Broody that his wife was buried in the adjacent grave, the one which was backfilled and mounded. To support what Brian had said, Thelma whipped a plank aside to prove that Mr. Broody had been staring into an empty grave. One dug in advance but yet to be used. Mr. Broody was still grudging and appeared unsatisfied, yet it was all quite obvious.

He thanked them and left the cemetery but they could see that he still was full of angst and disbelief. They knew that it was the impact of death and bereavement that stopped him thinking rationally. It was a familiar problem; people would do and say strange things in the aftermath of a death. Brian thought back to the previous week, when he had arranged a funeral for the late wife of the local milkman. He had suggested the following Friday to avoid any delay into the weekend. "That's not possible", the milkman replied, "I always collect the money on a Friday." The remark sounded callous so Brian commented that he must miss his wife a lot. "Yes," he replied, "I really do miss her. The house isn't the same; there's no smell of burnt toast."

Brian's mind was not really on Mr. Broody because he knew that this was an ideal opportunity to pump Thelma over the council's failure to obtain the chipboard coffins. He was confident that she was unaware that he had tipped off Ronson weeks earlier, and this was why the opportunity to obtain coffins had, suddenly and inexplicitly, dried up. But when he mentioned it to Thelma, he was surprised by the vehemence of her reply. Obviously irritated, she said, "You lot got at the manufacturer, you stopped us." But before he could respond, she continued, "Well, you still failed because Ben found an independent supplier down in the Midlands". Brian was aware that he was sneering when he said, "Bet you had to pay through the nose for those." "Yes," Thelma replied, "They were twice the price you pay for them but we'll still sell them much cheaper than you lot do." Brian was miffed, "So I suppose you will be flogging the DIY option and shoving the coffins in the back of some tatty van?" Thelma replied, with some confidence, "As a matter of fact a family did one last week and we had a lovely letter of thanks this morning. The family heaped praise on us, saying that they followed our leaflet, and, because there was no funeral director, they were able to do so much more themselves. It was really therapeutic and helped them come to terms with the death." Brian changed tack, "I heard that Ben had promised councillors that no coffins would be allowed to leave the cemetery on a car roof rack, yet at least one has been seen." Thelma just laughed.

Brian returned to the office, but was not relaxed. The independent funeral directors, those who would not join BALU, were troubling him. They could see the writing on the wall and were offering cardboard coffins without any hassle. Because of this, Ben was sending people who wanted a green funeral to them, and worse still, he was telling people that Flynn's would not use cardboard coffins. That was Brian's fault. He had actually said no to a family, confident that they would back down and use a chipboard coffin, but they didn't. It just encouraged them to go back to Ben and tell him what had happened. Brian wondered how long it would be before one or more BALU members reneged.

A few days later, whilst he was driving out of the cemetery, he saw Thelma inside the open doors of the disused burial chapel. He realised she was probably making up a cardboard coffin, one of their so called Brighton Caskets, because he knew it was where they were stored. He parked up, and went inside to find Thelma and another staff member handling a flat sheet of cardboard, about ten feet square. It was indented to enable them to fold the sides and ends, tucking them together to form the coffin base. As Brian watched intently, they showed him how they fitted webbing handles to the sides. Then, out came the flatpack lid, which was similarly folded into shape, and placed tightly over the base. They needled him over their ability to knock up one of the coffins in around ten minutes. Brian was irritated by the ease they displayed, and jibed, "You can't be serious, it's just a bloody great shoebox, it's so ugly." "No," said Thelma, "It's your coffins which are ugly, with their phoney veneer and plastic handles. At least people know what they are getting with these." Brian immediately realised that he was goading and not, as his wife kept reminding him, getting to the nub of the issue. Spontaneously, he pointed out to Thelma the first obvious weakness; there was no plastic sheet liner; it was bound to leak body fluids. She was prepared for this criticism and pointed out the gel coating inside, saying how they had tested it with some water and it did not leak. Brian was in no mood to listen and was determined to have the last word, "Well, if I have to use one, I'll make damn sure it leaks – even if I have to piss in it."

Brian binned the invite to the media event for the cardboard coffins, aware that none of the BALU members would attend. It was promotion for Ben's idea and there was no way they were going to be photographed endorsing these coffins. But he couldn't escape it because three days later, the Cumberland News hoardings read, 'Local coffins for Blue Army'. Emblazoned on the front page was a picture of artist Heather Harker, standing between her two painted coffins. There was no sign of stark cardboard. The first coffin was a riot of Carlisle United colours, with a team scarf draped over the head end. The second, she had illustrated on a more personal theme with paintings of her old British Leyland mini along both sides. Brian didn't want to read any more, but if he thought that was the end of it, he was mistaken; it was on every BBC local television news report that evening. He switched to Border Television but it was even worse. Their regular announcer not only talked over and praised the coffins, he declared to all the viewers that when his father had died, he had used the natural burial plot and a burial shroud rather than a coffin.

Brian recognised that it was media saturation and telephoned Ronson only to find out that it was far worse than he had imagined. The photographs had been syndicated all over the UK. They had been picked up by The Times, The Guardian, and all the southern editions of The Sun. A report was on London Radio, and The Big Breakfast Show actually had the painted coffins in the studio. They had even headed off for the sunny climes of Australia. Ronson told him that BALU head office were furious. It was not just the photos that upset them; it was the constant comments about why funeral directors had not offered such coffins in the past. Heather Harker, a provincial Cumbrian artist, had innocently managed to demean British funeral directing in the eyes of the entire world.

✝

Suddenly, Graham was being asked about painted coffins and burial shrouds and he wished he had taken more interest. The shroud had been in one of Ben's leaflets but he had thought it too outlandish. Now he looked inept. How was Ben's burial shroud different to the one that they used to dress a body in the coffin? He knew Thelma would tell him so he deliberately arrived early at his next burial, knowing she would be waiting to meet the funeral. "Thelma, why did you introduce this burial shroud?" Thelma replied, "Because some people told us that coffins appeared cold and harsh. Mothers, especially, feel that putting a baby or child into a coffin was the worst part of the funeral." Graham was surprised at this, and said, "I've never had anybody say that to me." "Well, you wouldn't would you because you're not listening." Graham then asked her why they had chosen wool and she replied, "Because they wanted something soft and cosy to wrap the body in, and Ben was keen because it's biodegradable and pollution free." "It's a new idea then?" said Graham. "No, not really", said Thelma, "You must have heard about the burial in wool acts?" No, he hadn't. "Well, for hundreds of years the government protected the English wool trade by dictating that burial must be in wool

54

and you paid a fine if Brussels lace or any foreign material was used. You see, Graham, we just went back into the past."

Thelma was in full flow, "We tried to source a burial shroud but nobody made them any more. We even tried those teaching spinning and weaving at the local art college but there was no interest in dressing the dead, so we decided to make our own. Ben went to Pearce's Mill and they had surplus stocks of undyed wool cloth. And then we managed to get black cotton ropes from a Kendal rope maker."

Graham said, "You make it sound like you knew what you were doing, but there were no designs available." "I know," said Thelma, "But Ben knew what was needed to make it work. That the body had to be placed on a board, and together, wrapped inside a large blanket that formed a sort of cigar shape. The ropes are stitched in place around the outside, to make it much easier to lift and move around and much easier than a heavy coffin."

"How on earth did you know it was going to work?" asked Graham. "If you really want to know," said Thelma, "Ben took the wool, ropes and board home one night and asked his wife to act as the corpse. He laid out the ropes, put the blanket over the top and stitched these together, and then his wife lay on the board." "Wasn't she bothered?" said Graham. "No," said Thelma, "She must have seen the funny side of it because she told Ben that she wouldn't be the first woman to play dead under a blanket." Graham actually laughed.

"So, it isn't at all like the shrouds we put on a body when it's laid in the coffin?" said Graham. "You mean those glitzy backless things more suited to a princess than a corpse. So many widows have told us that their husbands look as if they are dressed for a ball – as if prepped for the dance of death!"

†

Ronson walked down the High Street on his way back through the town, aware that his brow was permanently furrowed. In his little town there was not a person who would dream of using a cardboard coffin let alone a burial shroud; nobody would offend him by even asking. Yet up in Carlisle, movers and shakers, incited by Ben, were asking his members about the shroud and they looked to him for an answer. His wife had not stopped twining about it; how undignified; how corpse-like it appeared; how unhygienic. But it was she who had reminded him that if the problem was in Carlisle, then it was there that he needed to act.

Goaded by her, he telephoned the Environmental Health Department in Carlisle stating that he wished to report a potential health risk. His virtuousness swelled by the second as he was progressively transferred up to the head of department. He was conscious of gilding the lily but could not stop himself. After all, he was a time served funeral director and BALU was the principal organisation representing funeral directors. He complained, with some gravity, that the shroud would leak body fluids into the earth and cause pollution. The head man appeared very concerned, and said that he would investigate and get back to him within a few days. Ronson then called Roger, vindicated by his activity but a little too boastful and over confident of the outcome.

"There is no case to answer," said the Environmental Health Officer. "It seems to me that the danger of pollution is actually reduced when the shroud is used, rather than a coffin. And, because it's made of a natural material, it is going to last much longer and natural decomposition of the body is likely to be improved. It seems to me, that as the conventional coffins are chipboard rather than wood, they will break down in water far too quickly, so leakage into the soil is certain. In fact, the impervious plastic sheeting in these coffins probably pools up foul water and inhibits natural decomposition."

Ronson was furious. The man's words sounded just like Ben's. Then he realised they were Ben's. As the inventor and sole user, they must have gone straight to him; where else could they have gone?

He bit his lip! He knew that he had overplayed his hand and blamed his wife for the whole affair. He should never have contacted them. All he had done was to remind them of his profession's shortcomings. It was only about a year earlier that the EHO's had checked funeral director's facilities for embalming bodies and dealing with infectious disease. Subsequently, they had written to BALU to say that the facilities were inadequate. Worse, that some members had not been entirely truthful in their answers to questions. So, thought Ronson, even the EHO's are in Ben's camp.

CHAPTER SEVEN

Corpse Couture

"Have you seen the latest copy of the Colors magazine from Benetton?" said Roger to Ronson. "Benny who?" said Ronson. "It's an Italian firm called Benetton, they do women's clothing. It's their free magazine." "Roger, are you into cross-dressing or something? I haven't even heard of the firm let alone seen the magazine." Roger said, "Well, you'll want to see this. My daughter picked up a copy when she was in Carlisle. I'll show it to you before the meeting tonight."

So this was why two male funeral directors were engrossed in a women's fashion magazine, over a pint of beer. The entire magazine was about death. They could see no sense in linking death to women's fashion. Death had never been in fashion but Benetton, Roger's daughter had told him, had always courted controversy in their publicity. She had recalled the upset when they displayed a blood splattered newborn baby all over the billboards; that picture was the cover of an earlier Colors magazine. Written across the front of this copy was, 'Mort – un guide pratique (Death – a users manual)'. Inside, every page was about death. There were suicides, and deaths from the terrible Ebola Fever. There was every imaginable angle on death and funerals. Roger turned to a section headed: 'Fashion Victims – what the best-dressed corpses are wearing this season', and there, for all to see, was a beautiful, lithe,

Italian model. She was elegantly draped in Ben's burial shroud. Roger thought that this was surely the most novel way that Italian and English fashion had been linked since the Romans invaded Carlisle. Ronson thought, for a fraction of a second, that the model did, actually, look rather fetching.

"How on earth did this come about," said Ronson, on the assumption that Roger's snitches will have given him the lowdown, "How did Ben's burial shroud become a fashion icon?" They had to concede that however they looked at it, it was amazing. Roger suddenly realised that they had just complimented Ben, but he continued, "As far as I can tell, Benetton contacted him some months ago and asked if a wool shroud could be sent to their headquarters in Italy using an American courier firm. Heaven knows how Benetton found out about it, but it must have been all this media coverage. Apparently, there are fashion manufacturers all over the world who would sell their souls to get mentioned in this magazine, and then this cemetery upstart hits the jackpot.

Roger and Ronson joined the other members for their BALU meeting, and Ronson became animated about the Colors magazine. What was a local issue had become international, but after an hour everyone was sick to death of shrouds. Then, Brian described to them how Ben now takes one of their glitzy coffin shrouds on his talks to use as a prop. How, at the end of his talk, he whips it out and holds it up for all to see. He then tells everyone that it is a freebie with the chipboard coffins, and points out the shiny pink fabric and the lacy edgings around the seams. Widows, Ben tells them, hate to see their husbands in it. He calls it a blousy man-made fibre and then turns it around so that the audience can see that it is a backless garment. He explains how it's laid over the body

59

when it's in the coffin, and calls it the ultimate insult, or something like that. Then, with a flourish, he tosses the garment to the floor and says, 'I don't know about you, but I wouldn't be seen dead in that.' Everybody groaned.

Some days later, Roger telephoned Ronson. "Have you heard the latest news about this burial shroud going to Italy? "No, nothing," said Ronson. "Well, it seems that Ben is going around telling people that his bereavement service has the finest marketing slogan in the world; 'Carlisle Bereavement Services – We Send Shrouds to Turin!'

CHAPTER EIGHT

Die DIY

His father was immortal; Peter never expected him to die. It was a shock when his heart gave out; he was only fifty four. So much remained unspoken between them. Now, it was too late and he would never again hear his father's words. He struggled to recall their conversations as a way of holding on to him, no matter how tenuously. A further shock was the realisation that comfort and security were illusions; they were really his father's life force. With him gone he felt naked and lost. Then, there was the guilt of the survivor; of not saving him, and a failure to acknowledge what his father had meant to him. He had not done enough and now, it was too late. In this massive vacuum, he, as the eldest son, was now expected to lead the family. His first challenge was to arrange the funeral, something he had never experienced or even thought about. Of one thing he was certain, he would not hand everything over to a funeral director, not yet, anyway.

Peter talked constantly to his brothers, seeking the essence of their father. He knew his father had no religion, but he had a form of spirituality; what was it? Peter recalled a few things that his father had mentioned and from this he felt his inspiration. He had been a marketing man and he recognised and loathed the deceit of spiel. He had always wanted to be in control of his situation. Peter recalled that he had mentioned burial, he thought environmental burial, so the obvious thing to do was to talk to Ben West.

Peter asked the questions and Ben's answers told him that natural burial was right for his father. He had detested cant and there was honesty in a cardboard coffin that he knew would have appealed to him. Peter was surprised that there were four cardboard coffins to choose from; the Brighton Casket, the Peace Box and two types of Compakta coffin. Three had pseudo wood grain finishes but the cheapest Compakta had a white paper finish. When Ben said that he and his brothers could decorate this themselves, it was the coffin he chose.

Peter told Ben that he didn't want a vicar but there was only one non religious celebrant in Cumbria and he was a Humanist. This gave Peter another dilemma. His father might not be religious, but neither was he a Humanist. There was only one answer. He and his brothers would have to take the service themselves. Cost was also an issue. This was another reason why he was fearful of going to a funeral director. He knew that the package would push him to a hearse, embalming and a consultation, none of which he now needed. Armed with all this information from Ben, he telephoned an independent funeral director for a fixed price. Dad's body would be collected from the mortuary using an estate car and taken home in the coffin. He would be collected the next day and taken to the cemetery burial chapel an hour prior to the funeral service. It was all arranged in minutes. He was pleased, that way, nobody saw the vehicle, and they would walk beside dad's coffin, holding the bier, to the woodland plot. It would be a ritual walk.

They were glad to have the coffin at home, sitting on trestles in the lounge. There was no fear when it came to removing the lid. How could they be afraid of their dad? They were tearful, but too preoccupied to cry. There it was, the iconic coffin, its white blankness mocking them. The ease in which Peter had said that they would decorate it now seemed rash; what on earth would they put on it? There was banter, and mild arguments broke out, each brother having his own ideas, which the others then deflated. Dad's favourite cars, representations of his favourite places, items he treasured; all foundered. Then the youngest said, "Why not write on the coffin the things that dad used to say to us?"

The next day Peter stood outside the cemetery chapel ready to greet the mourners; dad's coffin already in the chapel. He felt nervous, in part because the funeral director had contacted Ben to suggest that the appearance of the coffin could upset the mourners. Ben had no qualms, don't worry, he said to Peter, all funeral directors prefer the, 'let's pretend it never happened,' kind of funeral.

Peter and his brothers lead the cortege, of about eighty mourners, many of whom he did not know, into the chapel. He then began the service by telling everyone about their dilemma the preceding day; a coffin bereft of decoration and the challenge of what to put on it. The youngest brother had suggested writing on the words that their dad regularly used, the everyday familiar words that immediately made him seem real and alive. Peter turned to look at the coffin, its length drawn out by large handwritten words, in black felt pen, 'Shut that bloody door!'

†

'Local taxi proprietor to facilitate DIY funerals,' said the newspaper item. "Idiot," Ronson said to himself, "He's so bloody naïve it's quite unbelievable. He had heard the rumours previously but couldn't believe them. He knew of this small taxi proprietor, who, as part of his business, also hired out limousines to funeral directors, but Ronson had never used him because he was based in Carlisle. The crack was already around that he had telephoned Ben to tell him that he had purchased a second hand hearse, which could be hired to people who wanted to do a DIY funeral. It would only be one hundred pounds, including the driver.

First, the coffin, and now the hearse. There won't be anything left at this rate. For many people, the coffin, with the hearse, was the funeral. If one could be hired independently, then their funeral package could be sidestepped. They all knew that conveying the coffin was a problem for people, with only the odd Volvo or Mercedes estate car being big enough; and vans! If they didn't know they could take the coffin in early, it needed some courage to roll up to the crematorium, in front of everyone, in one of those vehicles. A proper hearse gilds the funeral; there was nothing cheapskate about it.

Ronson telephoned one of his members, whom he knew hired limos from the taxi proprietor. A friendly, casual chat took place between this member and the taxi man. He was left in no doubt that his limo hire to funeral directors was at risk of being terminated! His hearse never carried a body. Ronson was on a role and then he had another idea.

'DIY Funerals are a Dead Loss – Undertakers', declared the newspaper hoardings all over Carlisle. Ronson was not impressed by the reporter's headline but felt elated at the impact of their BALU press release. Ronson and Roger had written this to emphasise that without a professional funeral director in attendance, DIY funerals appeared undignified and cheap and that this reflected poorly on the deceased.

Ronson felt pleased with the coverage, until Roger telephoned him five days later. "It's backfired! Two widows have written to the paper. I think Ben must have put them up to it." "What do they say?" said Ronson. "Too much," replied Roger, "They say BALU has no right to criticise them. That it's not a matter of cost, it's about personal involvement and freedom to do what they think is right." Ronson was immediately upset that BALU had been mentioned in their response; head office scanned all UK media and would pick up on it immediately. Roger continued, "Both women complimented the council on their initiatives. Then they poured scorn on us for saying that a funeral managed by the family could in any way lack dignity."

"I think we lost that one," said Roger.

†

Roger had just finished a funeral at the crematorium when he saw Ben standing out in the car park with a local solicitor, whom he knew, a big rugby player. He was a man who always attended the funerals of his clients, a personal touch quite rare with solicitors. But, Roger was puzzled when a white pick-up, that looked like a battered farm vehicle, pulled up, closely followed by a Transit van. The rear doors of the Transit were opened and a cardboard coffin was slid out. Four burly men then lifted it onto the back of the white pick-up. The rear panel hung down, loose and swinging, to enable the coffin to extend over the back end. Roger continued to watch as the four bearers, with Ben and the solicitor, walked behind the pick-up as it negotiated the drive that turned into the cemetery. Roger decided to follow, keeping them in sight. They headed, as he expected, for the natural burial plot, and as they approached, Roger could see that as many as one hundred and fifty mourners were assembled near the entrance. No funeral director, no hearse and no limos. It was a DIY job!

There were so many attending that Roger was able to tuck in, unnoticed, at the back. The four burly men, slowly and carefully, lifted the coffin out of the pick-up and carried it to the grave. The mourners were gathered round by the solicitor and Roger then realised that he was leading the service. He explained how the man, his friend, hated convention and had announced at the village pub that he wanted, "Four burly farm buggers to carry his coffin, using a pick-up and not a flashy hearse!" Everybody laughed and one or two murmured agreement.

Another friend, a workmate and the son-in-law were introduced, in turn, to reminisce about his friendship, his idiosyncrasies, his lifelong communism, his love of a joke over a pint. They related stories, some humorous, such as when he had worn flippers into a pub in Liverpool. More than a few swearwords slipped out. At times, the mourners were rolling about in riotous laughter, unselfconsciously and without embarrassment. The service ended and as people left, they shook hands with those who took the service. They laughed and joked and said that it was the best funeral they had ever attended.

Roger pondered, slightly bemused. What appeared at the start to be an undignified funeral, had turned out anything but. It was nothing like a normal funeral, there was no solemnity and yet nobody was offended in any way. He noted the mix of mourners, a few professionals, farmers and farm labourers, a few offcomers but the majority were Cumbrians through and through. It was interesting to see how the solicitor and family had participated and had been so comfortable. To him, it lacked polish but he could see it was full of emotion. But he felt much less threatened than he expected because what looked so easy was, in reality, quite difficult. This funeral only took place because the deceased demanded it, and there were confident people willing to make it happen. It was unusual, and he knew that the majority, out there, needed him, and would pay for him. He could live with DIY; it was not to be feared. But Roger knew that he had to keep his thoughts to himself; he could not be seen as a blackleg in BALU!

"The widow from Glasgow is waiting for you, I gave her a cup of tea," said his wife, when he returned to the office. Roger smiled knowingly at his wife and they both reflected on the inappropriateness of the word widow. It conveyed an image of a delicate, sensitive woman in mourning, distressed by the death of her husband, and in need of sympathy. But he knew that this woman was a harpie, and sympathy was an altogether alien word. She had a mouth that embarrassed truckers, and if the word fucking was ever banned then she would completely lose the power of speech. She had made an appointment to see Roger, and as her bile was directed at Ben, he forced himself to be a willing listener.

Roger had buried her late husband some months earlier. It was his second marriage. He had felt sorry for the poor man, assuming him to be both blind and deaf. He had found this harridan objectionable from the moment he met her, but a funeral was a funeral. She had, when making the arrangements, done everything in her power to cut out everyone associated with the first wife, not least her two 'fucking children'. Roger knew that it was her intention to return to Glasgow, no doubt, he thought, because she had fucking friends up there. What she had failed to tell Roger was that she had no intention of placing a memorial on the grave before she left, knowing that the two adult children would be deeply upset by this. Confident that she would not return to Carlisle, the children had erected a memorial on their father's grave, but without her permission, as the grave owner. Somehow, through a mischievous spy, she found out and had telephoned Ben to demand that the memorial be removed. Ben knew only too well that the law was on her side and that he would have to comply.

Roger was already aware of this miserable story because the two children had sought his advice, but he could do nothing. They then went to see Ben, anticipating that the memorial would have to be removed. It appeared that Ben had been very sympathetic, and as she would not speak to the children, Ben had agreed to mediate, unaware that it was with the devil. He telephoned her in Glasgow and asked if she would allow them to leave the small headstone on one half of the grave. This would leave the other side for a memorial to be placed by her, should she so wish. Her answer was no, but in Glaswegian!

It appeared that Ben licked his wounds for a few days, and then met the two children at the graveside to suggest a solution. As their father's grave was the last in the row, there was just enough space to add a small grave on the end. Their memorial could then be slid three feet to the left and off the grave owned by the harridan. The children were overjoyed, especially to be told that there was space in this small grave for their own cremated remains. They would then be adjacent to their father's burial; everybody was happy!

To show he had acted with due regard to her, as the grave owner, Ben sent off a letter to Glasgow, with a copy to Roger, stating that the unauthorised memorial had been removed from the grave. He neglected to say that it had only been moved three feet. Some weeks later she realised that she had been duped and immediately telephoned Ben with the opening line, "I suppose you think you are a fucking smart arse!"

Roger thought she had summed Ben up rather well but there was nothing he could do for her. She was not a happy harpie!

CHAPTER NINE

Curbing the Mud Slinger

"Did you watch him on News at Ten last night," asked Ronson. "Yes," said Roger, "They run to him the moment any funeral topic comes up." "I can't understand why, it's all the same stuff, everybody's heard it all before," said Ronson. "Ah," said Roger, "But everybody else when approached says no comment, whilst he can't wait to open his mouth and be in the limelight. He thinks he's a spokesman for the entire industry and they're happy to keep him there."

Ronson was perturbed; was all this media coverage spontaneous, or was it planned? Different topics arose, suddenly and without warning. He could anticipate nothing so there was no way he could be prepared. The BALU members met Ben's staff every day and inside information was picked up in dribs and drabs. Was it deliberate incitement? Was he, Ronson, developing a persecution complex?

Also, what they saw or heard would come to him second or third hand, with their own personal slant on it. But he noted that the mention of Ben always correlated with certain words; deluded; abusive; objectionable; aggressive; ghoulish. Then, one of the members joked that they should take out a gagging order on Ben, and that comment became Ronson's focus. A letter was necessary to go to Ben's employers demanding an end to his slanderous declarations.

Ronson felt sure of his ground and decided not to inform head office. Over a week he wrote down bits of the letter as they occurred to him. He preferred the word curb, because gag sounded too physical, and finally, the letter formed in his brain. His wife typed it out on the Remington, one finger at a time, as she did with all his letters. He signed it as the secretary of the Cumbria branch and then began telephoning his members, especially those who used the Carlisle facilities, asking them to add their signature. He was, though, shocked when it quickly became evident that although they were content to attack Ben anonymously through BALU, this was different. A signature was exposure; there could be repercussions. Those who went to Carlisle infrequently, signed, but the members in Carlisle, refused, all, that is, except Roger, the Vice President of the branch. Less than a tenth of the funeral directors using Ben's services would sign. It was a poor mandate. At a couple of firms, two or more people signed and a few signatures were actually unknown to him. But who would notice anyway, it was still impressive enough. The letter was dispatched to the Chief Executive of Carlisle City Council, and it read:

Dear Sirs,

The members of my Association have asked to write and forcefully express their irritation at the continuing abuse which is generated by one of you employees, Mr. Ben West. His outspoken Objectional attitude towards the Funeral Directors profession has now sunk to an all time low. Suffering from the delusion that he speaks for the community he needs to understand that what he says does not even represent a tiny minority. The media are as always exploiting his aggressive *outbursts and after the ghoulish appearance recently on national television a large number of Funeral Directors throughout the <u>Country</u> feel greatly insulted. His public expression that, 'Funeral Directors are only considerate in relation to the money which they can extract from their client', is deplorable and untrue. As his employer we, therefore, request you to curb his disgraceful attacks on our profession. If his remarks were not general they would be slanderous, and we have resisted the temptation of Media pressure to respond, for in doing so we may leave ourselves publicly accused of umprofessional conduct, as Mr. West has portrayed himself. Mud slinging is not the art of Professional people.*

Yours sincerely
Secretary of the Cumbria Branch BALU

†

The Chief Executive read the letter and his first reaction was to smile at the missing words and spelling errors. It looked very 'umprofessional!' Then he reflected on his father's funeral, which he had recently arranged in Bristol. It had not been a good experience; the fees charged were confusing and, inevitably, the final bill was much higher than he anticipated. He had questioned it but was left unsatisfied. Like most people, he suspected, he backed off because it was too sensitive.

The CE had also seen Ben on television and the reference to his ghoulish appearance was obviously absurd. Nonetheless, it was a serious accusation about one of his senior officers, so it had to be properly investigated. Ronson's letter was copied, and forwarded to Ben and his Departmental Director. A few days later Ronson had a reply:

Dear Mr. Neal,

Thank you for your recent letter concerning Mr. Ben West.

I am well aware of Mr. West's enthusiasm and commitment to providing an excellent service in Carlisle, and his desire to respond to the small but growing demand for alternative forms of funeral. The expansion of our operation to provide natural burial, biodegradable coffins, shrouds and advice on the organisation of funerals is in response to requests from the public, and is proving a great comfort to people who feel ill at ease with traditional arrangements. At the same time, the standard of service to those who choose the customary forms of disposal has not diminished and we continue to provide a service which, in my opinion, has no equal in the region.

I have an assurance that Mr. West did not make the comment which you have attributed to him in your letter, and your observations simply reveal the other side of a vigorous debate within the profession. That seems to me to be a healthy position between individuals who all share in common a concern for the services to the bereaved.

So long as our services are being expanded to offer greater choice in response to demand, and yet maintain their excellent standards, I can find no cause for complaint against Mr. West.

†

Ronson realised that Ben was not to be curbed and he now regretted the letter. It had split the BALU members into two divergent camps; those who signed and those who didn't. But there were other niggling issues that had disturbed him and put him in an ill humour. One was Flynn's, who had upset a family by refusing to use a cardboard coffin. As he anticipated, they went straight to Ben and the crack was everywhere.

Then the media in Newcastle put the finger on one of their members after a Geordie son had arranged the funeral of his late father and it turned out a dismal experience. This, in itself, was hardly groundbreaking news, but it was taken to another level. The man announced that he was so offended, that he was going to become a funeral director himself. Not only was he rubbishing conventional funeral directing and their high prices, but he was promoting green funerals. Naturally, the media linked him with Ben; it was double trouble for BALU.

Ronson was sick of the whole bloody business; it was 'doing is ed in', as one of his staff would say. His name stank at head office, with Cumbria the place where funeral directing had lost its grip. And now there was another new and potentially more serious matter; Bill Roberts had sold out to one of the big funeral companies. This was the first sale he had experienced of a family firm to one of the big companies, and it worried him. The family firms were the heartbeat of BALU and there was one thing that had always united them; they were all part of their community. The corporate firms did nothing for community. Ronson felt it was the beginning of the end.

He spoke to Roger and the owners of other family firms to gauge their feelings, but all they could say was, let's wait and see what happens. He didn't need to wait and see, he knew what had happened down south. It caused so much friction between BALU members that the family firms had been forced to cut loose and form an alternative funeral directing association. They, and BALU, were now at each others throats. He also felt sorry for Graham. He was going to be acting manager for the first six months, and Bill was to work with him over this period in order to smooth the transfer of the business. Ronson knew how these companies operated; Bill would detest the new ways and would be hell to work with.

CHAPTER TEN

Reiving Roberts

Bill finally signed on the dotted line, and sold out. Although the funeral premises were included, the real value was in the goodwill, as it was so inappropriately called. It was the payment made to Bill by the new company, a sum for each and every anticipated funeral. He slept restlessly thinking of the unknowing families returning to the trusted Roberts's, hoodwinked, because the family name was still over the door, as if nothing had changed. They would be unaware that they were now the historic customer base, with their corpses transfigured, exalted even, onto a corporate balance sheet. Over the entrance it really needed a warning; 'caveat corpus' (body beware!)

Bill had to justify the decision to himself; he knew that he had betrayed local people and local businesses. He had betrayed his father, who created the firm, a man who hated big, anonymous companies. Yet Bill, as a prominent BALU funeral director, had now enabled a big corporate firm to obtain a foothold in Carlisle. His was the first nail in the BALU coffin.

Bill knew that they would suck still more income out of the goodwill. Even if people realised that the firm had been taken over, they would assume that the new firm still possessed the principles of the past. It was odd, this nationwide firm carried out thousands of funerals so logic suggested reduced prices; wasn't that why takeovers occurred? But no, he knew that they were one of the most expensive funeral directing firms in the UK. Sure enough, within days, he was told that they had increased his funeral package by over a hundred pounds despite it being exactly the same. It made him feel even worse when one of his previous employees told him he felt like a criminal making such high charges.

Bill hated the thought of having to witness these changes during the six months transfer period. It would hurt but this was the future of funeral directing. The premises looked like it always did, but there was a new culture beneath the surface; it was now an outlet, one of many outlets in the UK. Neither did a funeral director like himself run the show; an accountant in an office in Manchester dictated terms. The funerals became anonymous figures on a financial spreadsheet. The staff changed overnight into puppets, their strings pulled by a regional manager. He watched as, progressively, all of his local business contracts were ended. The firm had their own coffin manufacturer, and national floristry and memorial arrangements. They called it vertical integration; in reality, it was part of the insidious destruction of Bill's community.

Bill knew it would be bad but it was worse than he expected. His clients, now their clients, were to experience a process familiar all over the UK; a packaged outlet offering a packaged funeral, with packaged language, packaged staff and packaged products. The British didn't realise that this was to be their new way of death. It was painful to watch knowing that he was the cause. He was now just a token presence, a dissembler to conceal reality. He could no longer speak on behalf of the company unless the words were first agreed. He was now contractually barred from opening or being associated with another funeral director within one hundred miles of Carlisle. Perhaps worst of all, he had to defer to younger and less experienced staff, who often spoke only corporate spiel. That included his previous employee and underling, Graham, who was now acting as the temporary manager. Bill did as much as he had to, and no more. He constantly embarrassed Graham by harping on about how things were done in the past, despite knowing that he had no choice but to do things differently under the new regime.

The new regime was all about sound bites like, added value, which really meant how to squeeze more out of the bereaved. It stuck in Bill's craw that although he had not provided cheap funerals, he had never been this greedy. Now there was the expectation to sell the bereaved bigger and better, whether coffins, wreaths, funeral teas, anything, just as long as income went up. There were targets, never stationary but constantly moved, and always upwards. His father had always said that there was a delicate balance between the funeral cost and being seen to be taking advantage of the bereaved. On the tip of his tongue were Ben's words, it's a rip-off, but he couldn't quite go there.

†

Graham had tried hard to avoid being the temporary manager, but it was that or nothing. As the weeks passed, his impotence in the role caused him real frustration and stress. It came as no surprise that he could not manage Bill and that he would just have to sit out his six months carry over. But what really surprised him was the frustration when dealing with the bereaved. His outlet experienced something unknown in other outlets and peculiar to Carlisle; people rang up wanting a funeral price.

It was BALU policy not to advertise funeral costs, and it suited the firm to accord with this. But Ben's acolytes were encouraged to phone around various local funeral directors to obtain quotes, and if they called Graham, he realised he was hamstrung. He was not allowed to give a price and he knew exactly how it would play out. Ben always advised them to make the last call to the entrepreneurial Roger, stalwart and Vice President of BALU, and he would always, without exception, give a lower quote than any of the others. Graham knew he did this; all the funeral directors knew he did this; but nobody did anything about it. A restrictive practice can only work, he thought, if everybody supports it.

If Graham struggled, then he knew Roger had it sussed. He called it the telephone price. Once a price was given, the bereaved usually rang off but if they returned days later, they had to be recognised and the promised telephone price honoured. So the name of the enquirer, the date and the quote, had to be meticulously recorded. Otherwise, the danger was that the staff would deal with the enquirer as if they were new and mention dearer prices, which would be embarrassing. Graham found himself envying Bill's previous autonomy. He had always refused telephone quotes because it demanded that he broke down his funeral price, but then Bill had neither targets nor company policy to contend with. And a telephone quote necessarily had to include the cheapest coffin, but that had implications on other company policy; the need to sell more of the expensive coffins.

This first class service now needed a first class, glossy

brochure, and, out of the blue, that duly appeared. The sentiments expressed on the first page were a promotional master class on company values and the desire to extend choice. To reflect this, what better than a wide range of high quality coffins? Further pages then extolled the models, each posed by a promotional eye. The backdrop was all visual appeal with velvet drapes, masses of expensive flowers and, to imply a pseudo Christian aura, an occasional cross or crucifix slipped into the picture. The deep brown, almost black, veneers, were hinting at expensive rainforest timbers. The nameplates were all blank and Graham noticed other blanks; words like plastic and chipboard were missing!

As if the brochure was guilty of underselling, company policy dictated that the coffins must be displayed in a showroom, and this, too, was a fine art. Coffins sitting on trestles were unacceptable as they would make the room look like a mortuary. And, to their marketing expert, an entire coffin looked too morbid; too ready to accept an occupant. Perhaps they employed a psychologist in marketing, thought Graham, somebody who suggested that half a coffin would look less accommodating; that the psyche would fail to make a connection with a dead body. Whatever the reasoning, the policy was to slice each coffin, diagonally, in half, and mount them all on one wall, side by side. Graham couldn't fail to be impressed, but his psyche immediately suggested that it looked like a churchyard landslip; the coffin ends poking out of a row of exposed graves. But there they were, sliding out of the painted wall; cheapest to the left and seven coffins along, the dearest. Also, the veneers were graded, lightest to the left and darkest to the right, like a Dulux colour chart. Somebody, the psychologist perhaps, had clearly identified the tone of the veneer as indicative of quality. Yet Graham knew that the production price between all of the coffins varied only by a few pounds.

Bill was apoplectic again. He kept reminding Graham that when he first started in the business they only offered one coffin, there was no choice. It was just a component of the funeral, a utilitarian container for a body; it was not disembodied and mounted against a damned wall!

As would be expected of an expert on coffins, Graham studied the handles. Sure enough, there was a subtle promotional touch over their selection. Less substantial handles with a silver finish were fitted to the lighter veneers, with bulkier, brass finished handles to the darker veneers. Somebody had considered visual appeal; somebody who knew that the bereaved would see the darker coffins, with their brassy handles, as higher quality. But the handles were all plastic, purely decorative, and hardly more than a fiver a set. They could never be used to carry the coffin.

The mounted coffins didn't arrive solo. Each was accompanied by its own sales data sheet and trailed a target. Staff training sessions solely on the selling of coffins began, and the regional manager introduced a new language. Words like 'upselling' and terms like 'added value' soon became familiar; Graham understood marketing spiel but he could see that some of his staff found it difficult to embrace.

The nub of the training was that the cheapest coffin had to be subtly degraded so that the bereaved, without evident pressure, moved up the line. They had to do this purely because they believed that it was giving the deceased a better send off. How could the bereaved know that they were paying perhaps one hundred pounds extra for the next coffin, when it had cost not two pounds more to buy in? Some staff found it expedient during their training to call the lowest priced coffin the 'poor' one, but that word was banned; none of their coffins were other than the finest quality. In their marketing parlance, they were good, better and best. So this was the American approach, thought Graham, the one that they would now have to live with. It was the one so derided in Jessica Mitford's book, 'The American Way of Death'.

These untagged coffins needed a promotional name and, 'The Lincoln' or 'The Gatsby' wouldn't work in Britain, so somebody had decided to give them royal lineage. 'The Sandringham' was the cheapest, 'The Balmoral' the mid range, and 'The Windsor' the most expensive. When the staff first heard these names, they were, privately, met with typical British humour. "As if the Queen would be buried in a crappy chipboard job," summed up the banter. But Graham recognised that it also summed up the British; they always saw the irony. Whereas the American employee adopted, believed in and even proselytised about their promotional panache and company policy, the British would just mock its pretensions.

The trainers were ready for the British employee. They had anticipated that British staff might think it morally decent to suggest to a widow that as the Balmoral was little better than the Sandringham, why spend more than they need to? To counter this flaw, the emphasis was put on their personal responsibility, that it wasn't just about their targets and commission; poor sales let down the entire team.

At first, Graham found the targets relatively easy to achieve but as time passed they became ever more ephemeral. At his last meeting, the regional manager had instructed that he wanted a 40% increase in the sales of the Balmoral and a 10%

increase in the Windsor over the next quarter. The target was reached but they then realised that with the reduced sales of the Sandringham, the cheapest coffin was dropped off the end of the line. All the other coffins slid down one place making room for the Buckingham at the top end. This caused consternation because the good, better and best had shifted one place, which was difficult to remember. Graham and all the staff soon realised that they would have to live with increasing targets, as well as the occasional reshuffle nudging the cheapest coffin off the end. Then, somebody mentioned they were running out of palatial names; perhaps the new top end coffin should have an environmental theme – the Highgrove, perhaps!

CHAPTER ELEVEN

The Chain of Fraternal Friction

It was the most glamorous event of the year, the annual Embalmers Institute dinner at the opulent Abbey Hotel. Ronson knew the embalmers liked to play: they were the life and soul of any party! He parked up and negotiated a chicane of plush Bentleys, Jaguars, Mercedes and Porsches. Any casual visitor would assume this to be a wealthy businessman's conference, and, impressed by German engineering, they might miss the defining vehicle registration plates; DED 1 and DED 2!

It was the last of the years fraternal events at which the Presidents of every Institute in the business would gather. Each attended one another's annual dinner as an honoured guest; it was a brotherhood. Kind sentiments were expected, and praise related to the years and years of dedication lavished on the bereaved. This unwritten convention had developed over seventy years and each President, through word and deed, was expected to stay within the confines of their own sphere of work. Ben had already broken that convention; fraternally, he was not welcome.

Ronson stood, as the Presidents, adorned in their chain of office, were slow hand-clapped into the banqueting room, a gowned lady on their arm. A toastmaster ceremoniously introduced each personage on the top table, stretching out right and left from the Embalmer's President in the centre. The fraternal etiquette was well rehearsed; those most beloved in closest proximity to the hosting President; those least beloved on the periphery. Ronson is surprised. Ben and his wife are not terminally seated; they are inset by two places. The terminal two were from a company who made wreaths. The reason, whispered around the table, was that they had upset the men in black; something had been said in flowers, but offensively.

As Ronson enjoyed his gourmet meal, it was regularly called to a halt, mid mouthful, by a request from the President to 'take wine' with each branch present in the room. With every bobbing up and down to take wine, the expectation grew for the table to do more than merely raise a glass. Entertainment began to accompany the bobbing, with the Yorkshire Branch giving a rousing rendition of Ilkley Moor Ba'Tat – twice! As the evening progressed, the fine wine coursed through the veins and loosened the limbs, and many an embalmer looked pickled!

The embalmers never let them down over the entertainment, and, true to form, this year it was to be Janet Brown, the international comedienne. The jollity of the evening would imply unity, thought Ronson, but the conflict would still simmer beneath the surface. In his cosy glow, he settled back and while waiting for her to begin, scanned the room, looking at the old timers and the new. The old timers, like him, who called a spade a spade, would always call embalming – embalming! It used to be an art, but it was getting a dirty name. The new ones didn't do embalming; they did hygienic treatment. They represented big funeral directing firms, and had hijacked the Institute in recent years. Hygienic treatment, it sounded necessary, clean and clinical, so needed a premium price; but it was really no different to embalming. Perhaps, in the future, they would have to call their President the Hygienic President!

He could see Ben, resplendent in his chain of gold leaves. It had been lucky for Ronson and Roger that Ben's Institute conference had been in Carlisle so they had been able to attend. They had actually enjoyed the talk from the environmentalist Chris Baines, all about thinking globally and acting locally, looking at your own work and its impact on the environment. There was no way Chris Baines would be invited to speak to the embalmers, thought Ronson.

Ben's address, at his conference, was, as Ronson expected, confrontational. Even mildly inebriated, Ronson recalled his statements. There were too many funeral directors and not enough bodies, and prices were kept artificially high. Then, he had had his Monty Python moment when he asked the room what funeral directors had done for the bereaved in the past fifty years. And Ben didn't like the obituary columns, which only complimented the funeral director and ignored the minister and Ben and his services. And then, to top it all, he said that he was going to write a Charter – a Charter for the Bereaved. Let's hope, thought Ronson, that it will just involve his own lot and leave us alone.

After the impressive star turn, people began to drift off. He noticed Ben and his wife going back to their guest suite, all paid for by the men in black. Such an opulent setting would be a treat for him, thought Ronson. Ben's Institute dinners were a lesson in parsimony, usually set in salubrious council facilities; a sport's hall! On one notable occasion, it was at a swimming pool complex. At least, he thought, the smell of chlorine would have made the Embalmer's President feel at home, and have suggested hygiene; then the food turned up frozen and uncooked! And, there was the conference at Felixstowe Leisure Centre. The one where the entertainer was Percy Edwards – doing bird impressions!

Thank God, thought Ronson, that the embalmers knew how to party.

CHAPTER TWELVE

The Tame Minister

Ronson loved Cumbria because it lived in times past; he felt it was immune to change. When he perambulated through his little town hardly a person passed by who did not speak or acknowledge him. A glimmer of Dickensian life remained that considered the mainstay of the community to be the Church of England minister, the doctor and the funeral director. One maintained spiritual health, the other rude health, and the last disposed of the corrupt remains. But he was suddenly struck by the breadth of his role within this parochial trilogy. The doctor took no heed of the minister's role; the minister no heed of the doctors: yet his role was intricately associated with the impact of the other two.

As he walked, the doctor's failure was too obvious. The abundance of walking sticks, the obesity, even in the young, all evidence that peoples' health was very poor. They lived longer but ailed for decades. The town possessed a myriad of sickly old folks, who, when they met him, lapsed into a meditation, his acquaintance a potent reminder of the fragility of life. He knew intimately who had experienced heart attacks; those who had high blood pressure, and what medication they were on. They had no talisman to protect them, so they fended him off verbally, usually by saying, "I'm not ready for you, not just yet anyway!"

The minister's failure was similarly evident, but only to him. As Ronson worked below the surface, he saw the religious doubt insidiously creeping everywhere. Unlike the C of E minister, he actually met and worked with all religions, and the atheists, so he had a much broader understanding. The Victorians had been convinced that society would collapse without the Christian religion, but he knew otherwise. The town might be physically dominated by its church, but it was sparsely frequented on Sundays; the locals were not God fearing.

As he headed to the office, Ronson's brain was on BALU issues, in particular the delicate relationship between the funeral directors and C of E ministers. This religious awakening had been prompted by Ben; he was romancing the clergy! He looked for their support because they had common interests in the community. He also played on the fact that their role, especially in funerals, was being undermined by funeral directors, so he deferred to them and valued their opinions. Ronson sensed that Ben's tactics were working, not that there was anything really concrete to judge this by. It was just that on his funerals and in conversations with the ministers he met daily, he sensed a slight change, there was more than a hint of antagonism towards them.

What was obvious was their support for what Ben was doing. Ronson suspected that they had been taken out of their vacuum and fired up. BALU will have been denigrated, painted as opposed to change and to low cost funerals. It appeared that the clergy had adopted Ben; an atheist St. George, to fight the BALU dragons!

Ronson and the other members were often closeted in the hearse with the clergy for long periods. Now, many ministers used that opportunity to mention what was happening in

Carlisle. They would goad and tease, even pontificate, on the issues or the media coverage, fully aware of how it was impacting on the local funeral directors.

Ronson knew that some ministers actually disliked their local funeral directors, but it had not previously bothered him. He was convinced that they were envious of the big money funeral directors were making whilst the clergy lapsed into poverty. He couldn't meet a minister these days without them harping on about how their lives were a dichotomy. They were pillars of the community, occupied an imposing vicarage for forty years, and were then dumped in retirement, on a poor pension and homeless.

The poor pension, thought Ronson, created the tame minister, and it was almost certainly the cause of all the antagonism. It was only when he reflected back, that he realised how much things had changed. As recent as the 1960's, the local minister had been a big noise in the community, often an intimidating scholar from Oxford, and funeral directors had deferred to them when it came to arranging funerals. They would never have thought of arranging a cremation or burial without first contacting the minister. When was he free; what suited him best? But, in recent years this had all been reversed, and the BALU members had contributed to the weakening of the minister's position in the community. Their deference ceased and many were now routinely ignoring the minister by arranging the funeral service, even the hymns, directly with the bereaved family. To compound the insult, they often arranged the funeral on a day and time to suit the availability of the hearse and cars, then presented the funeral arrangement to the minister as a fait accompli.

The minister then had a dilemma. If he or she quibbled over whether it was convenient or not, they knew what the response would be; that the family were quite content for the funeral director to arrange another minister. It was the potent threat of having a tame minister hiding in the wings, ready to perform at a minutes notice. They were retired clergy, who allied themselves to specific funeral directors, and were willing and available to do services at any time. Despite knowing that service fees were an essential component of the parish minister's stipend, these tame ministers actively sought funeral services as income – the notorious ash cash!

It had to stop; the clergy needed to be brought back on board. Ronson put the item on the BALU agenda knowing that the members would not be sympathetic; their response would be to question his judgement. It was not about religion any more, it was all about a good performance. People wanted the Christian pretence, but without the religion, and the funeral directors were just responding to this. People were paying a hefty minister's fee, so why shouldn't they get what they wanted? They wanted warm words, and pleasant sentiments said about the deceased; they even wanted the deceased to be referred to by name. The last thing they wanted was a zealous minister, the ones who said that the funeral was all about God. Why should the funeral director feel guilty if they found a personable retired minister, one that they liked, one who would perform as they wanted, one who played to the gallery, one who needed the fee?

He suspected that at the BALU meeting, members would emphasise how difficult their parish minister was. That he or she insisted on meeting the family, to discuss the service, but in essence it would just make the family uncomfortable over their failure to attend church; there was no way they wanted these ministers to do their funerals. A zealous minister could reflect poorly on the firm. Then these funeral directors would tell him how uncomplicated it was to use the new Humanist celebrant in Carlisle, how he did what the family wanted, they just paid him and parted company, it was neat and tidy. They would insist that this was what the British wanted at their funerals. So as Ronson prepared his papers for the BALU meeting that evening, he suspected that his good intentions would be frustrated; there would be no going back.

CHAPTER THIRTEEN

Pariahs Pinking Up

Roger took his wife to Paris for a weekend, and returned refreshed. Cumbria might have clean air and beautiful scenery, but it was dullsville in winter. Even his son had recently told him that the Royal Shakespeare Company had defined Cumbria as culturally deprived and intended to put on special performances for the natives. Roger could see the funny side of that; it would be entertainment for the offcomers, like Ben.

For Roger, as a funeral director, holidays were always an experience in wariness and Paris had been no different. When he met people outside the world of funerals, normal people that is, he took great care and was always on the defensive. He knew that, sooner or later, strangers would pose the question; what work did he do? He wondered whether his reticence to mention work actually promoted curiosity. Roger dreaded these confrontations, because many a promising holiday friendship would suddenly take a downturn. Once exposed, he became socially volatile because those present would be in one of two camps, and neither was enjoyable. The first camp was those who, with a flourish of the hands, would exclaim loudly, "Oh, let's not go there, it's too horrible." The conversation, and the relationship, would promptly end. At times, he had actually seen fear in the eyes of those who acted this way. There was no mediator, no intermediary, no counsellor, the conversation just ceased, often with an embarrassing silence.

To ease their feelings of rejection, he and his wife, who was also snubbed, would console themselves with the belief that these people were full of vanity; they could not accept ageing let alone death. They were people who had to look perfect, with their manicured nails, perfect hair and a liking for cosmetic surgery. It was everywhere and it was getting worse year on year. They were people with a craving for immortality, yet had no idea what to do with themselves on a wet Sunday afternoon. It was the new religion, one which had exchanged prayers for scalpels and expensive wrinkle cream. Roger almost felt sorry for them because he knew that they were the ones who would not write a will, who would create phobias in their children, and make death far more of a problem than it should be within their families. But it was still upsetting for Roger, as it was for other funeral directors, when they were similarly rejected because of their work.

Roger was no happier with people in the other camp, those with a morbid fascination for death. They were the ones who would all too often, finding out what he did, say that they had always wanted to be a funeral director. If not that, then they always wanted to be a bloody embalmer! These people were a problem for a different reason. It was as if they sensed that working in the death business gave him an insight into the secrets of the netherworld. That he knew something of profound consequence, which even he might have failed to recognise. So they probed, questioned, sought they knew not what and were often troubled by his responses. Roger felt that these would be the kind of people who sought the meaning and purpose of life. It was conspiracy theory, the thought that something was going on, just below the surface. Roger often enjoyed chatting to these people, but not on holiday. Every time he subsequently met them, a death topic would be raised, something they had thought of in the night. A deep and meaningful conversation would then ensue, stretching from religions to suttee, when all he and his wife wanted was a friendly chat. There was no relaxation in it. The mantle of the untouchable, the pariah, could not be thrown off.

The strange thing was that Roger did know the meaning of life; it was a short period in the sunshine, and an eternity in oblivion. The thought actually filled him with contentment; the peace of it all. It was because he saw too many religions, too many opposing beliefs, too much small mindedness, too much human misery. He was confident that no God existed but he kept it to himself.

Later that day, as he chatted to a widow, his eyes filled with tears. Was it genuine or did he have to recall a moment of personal distress, like an actor on a stage? Would it have to be something really unpleasant, his circumcision, perhaps? Whatever the trigger, it never failed to impress. Today the widow explained how her late husband had died, "He had just fetched the coal in. He loved to see the coal scuttle full!" she said. Roger's tears dripped off his chin. Her husband had suffered a stroke, but was alive on arrival at hospital. Robbed of the power of speech, he was unable to communicate with his wife of sixty years. Unsure if he could even hear her voice, her last memory of him was in a hospital bed, attached to tubes and monitors, surrounded by strangers. She had wanted him to come home again, even if it was to die. She knew it would have made some difference to her last memory of him; she saw it as a personal failure at a critical time.

The way she opened up like this reminded Roger of why he was such a good funeral director. He was not just a listening ear but a friend and trusted advisor, yet he could not have spent more than twenty minutes in her company or on the phone. Despite such little contact, she had total confidence in him. He could allay her fears about viewing her husband's body and about how nice he would look if dressed in his best suit. The word embalming would not be mentioned by him so she would see no need for it. It was just as well because Roger found the process distasteful and always tried to avoid it. It was all a question of confidence.

It was so easy, so gentle, when they were not embalmed, not all pinked-up by chemicals. It was easy for Roger's staff too. All they had to do was ensure that her husband's body was washed, his mouth and eyes closed, and any stubble shaved from his face. After putting on his favourite suit that his wife had wanted him to be dressed in, a small amount of make-up would be applied to his face, and his hair combed. His widow could have done it herself, had she so wished.

He never told his clients that he hated the process of embalming. Unlike most funeral directors, he didn't do it automatically as part of a package. On those rare occasions when people actually asked, he still tried to convince them otherwise. It was the chemicals; if they were manufactured to delay putrefaction then they had to be damned toxic. So toxic, that some of the old funeral directors, who had contracted rare cancers, blamed it on exposure to the chemicals.

It was the fault of the Americans. The British had never felt it necessary until they introduced it. It was so Hollywood. The gangster films with their gory murders, the next minute the corpse looking picture perfect in a massive velvet lined casket. Roger was repulsed when he first saw how the Americans couched their bodies. The corpse could not look like a corpse. The body, after embalming, was immaculately dressed in a dinner jacket and bow tie, or a beautiful gown, and then positioned resting on an elbow, reclining on a chaise-longue. There was the ultimate smile on the face, the lips stitched in place using a needle and thread. With the star prepped, the presentation of the body was nothing other than a film set. Serene music was played, and the bereaved relatives ushered in, the corpse was positively blooming. The complexion was perfect, the cheeks blushed by a beautician to a healthy rose pink; the corpse looking far better dead than it ever did alive!

Roger was thankful that the Brits were as repulsed by couching, as he was, even if they were conned into accepting embalming by most funeral directors. He had always managed his business without embalming, just as they all did up to the 1970's and before the American invasion. It was all a matter of confidence.

†

Graham was now, in American speak, part of the death care industry. The BALU members, the ones who advertised themselves as builders or carpenters, with funeral directing as a sideline, appeared like dinosaurs. They were funeral directors only through utility, purely because they had once possessed the skill to construct a coffin. It was a skill the Americans would see as quaint, yet pathetic. Even his earlier experience at Roberts's now seemed nonchalant when compared to the American approach; quaint English funeral directing had been yanked into the real world.

Back in those days, he had had a free hand in his work. Few people questioned anything he advised. If they showed even a hint of opposition or discomfort, he could just back off. There was nobody really watching, and no commission or targets. It didn't matter if an occasional embalming was lost, or viewing of the body refused. The approach by the new firm was entirely different, but was so cleverly presented that it still looked traditionally British and long established.

The company now considered the time served role of the funeral director as outdated; too much emphasis had been put on a personal relationship and not on salesmanship. Clients would now meet a salesperson, but their name badge said, Funeral Arranger. This new role attracted people skilled in the selling of services and products, often with no previous knowledge of the funeral world. The traditional male dominance of the funeral director shifted to the female dominance of the funeral arranger; women with innate communication skills and an air of integrity.

The diminished role of the funeral director meant that they now only took charge of the funeral from the moment it left the premises for the cemetery or crematorium. Their role was limited to presentation; they were dressed to look like a funeral director but hadn't previously met the family and knew nothing of the relationship between the body in the coffin and those alive in the limousines. The funeral director felt vulnerable in this anonymous role so they gleaned what information they could beyond the simple names of the deceased, and the next of kin. They had to get this information from the only person who knew it, who controlled it; the Funeral Arranger, the person who told you sweet FA!

For Graham, salesmanship was now the driving force.

Viewing the body was considered essential and viewing a body that had not been hygienically treated was unacceptable to the company. A single viewing during office hours, and hygienic treatment, was costed into the funeral package, but the company knew that viewing, especially in big families, could gain a momentum of its own; an evening viewing was extra; a weekend viewing was extra; multiple viewings were extra. Viewing was all about optional extras.

He found that people accepted the need for viewing and hygienic treatment. Hygienic treatment, they knew nothing about the procedure and they asked nothing. The words alone carried professional weight, implied necessity. It was all so easy and the danger, perhaps, was to become blasé about it.

It was, then, unusual when the funeral arranger referred Mrs. Ralphs to Graham because she did not want her husband's body to be viewed. She said that he would not have wanted all and sundry looking at him and she preferred to remember him as he was in life. Graham knew that the company would see her failure to view as his failure. They called it the memory image; a psychological need to recollect a serene dead husband in his coffin. She had to understand that everybody viewed the deceased these days, that great solace would be gained from this final farewell, that it was the last chance for her, the family and friends to say goodbye.

As he spoke, Graham watched for signs of weakening but none was apparent. So he reminded her that the option for one viewing was included in the funeral price so it would be no problem to let it stand. This seemed to confuse her, and although Mrs. Ralphs never actually said yes, the viewing box was ticked. Although when they parted she was not really at ease, this was not unusual with funeral arrangements.

What was unusual was that Mrs Ralphs returned the following day with an air of confidence; it suggested a remonstrance. Did they intend to embalm her husband, she wanted to know? When Graham heard the word embalm, he knew that he had a problem because the word had never been mentioned. But how much did she know? He avoided saying yes, suggesting that embalming was all about preservation, and that their treatment, their hygienic treatment, was all about sanitising the body, so that it was no longer a health risk. Had he said enough? Was she weighing what he had said against her source of advice; was it Ben and his staff? She wasn't satisfied. She knew that there was no health risk from his body and felt that she was being deliberately mislead. Then she asked him outright whether their treatment meant pumping formaldehyde into his body. It was with the word formaldehyde that Graham returned to his training; what to do with an intractable customer. It was all set out; first, apologise; second, express the case for a misunderstanding; third, refund a sum to account for the disputed work. The training manual was confident that this would avoid a formal complaint.

The company training had also taught him that occasional customer resistance was to be anticipated. If two in a hundred demurred, then ninety eight were compliant with company policy. It might not be a failure in their sales technique, they had been told, it could just be an affliction in the person, such as necrophobia. It was a word that fascinated him; an irrational fear of death and dead bodies. The word irrational also puzzled him; what did it mean? Turning it around, what exactly was a rational fear of death? People could watch the goriest images on a screen but the seeing and touching of a real corpse, even a loved one, appeared to terrify them.

Whether it was necrophobia or something similar like coffin phobia, the need to view the body still had to be promoted. It was all about commission and yet, personally, Graham disliked it. It was rarely satisfying for the staff because too much emotional tension surrounded the occasion. The act of viewing was entirely incidental to the main play; being seen to do the right thing. Not so much to see the deceased as to be seen seeing the deceased. Some felt they were under an unspoken obligation to be there. Some would be bullied into going. Some would see it as a declaration of their loyalty and love. Some felt obliged to go because they had a claim on the estate. Then there was the problem of bad blood in the family, when the widow or widower didn't want certain relatives or friends to be there. When the blood was really up, they banned people from attending and this gave Graham a real problem; he had to check that people were entitled to view. Sometimes, people turning up were completely unknown to the family, assumed to be known only to the deceased. The friend, who worked with the deceased, became a handy euphemism!

Another euphemism was the room they called the Chapel of Repose. It was another American import that the British had accepted, but Graham found it all rather pathetic. It was always a tiny room, with so little space that the obligatory wood cross, a dictate of company policy, had to be mounted on the wall because there was nowhere else it could go. Another wall would display artificial flowers, another company dictate replicated in all their other outlets. A heavy velvet curtain would cover one wall, intended to give the room the aura of a chapel.

Graham recalled the first time he had entered the Chapel of Repose. There was an odour, strange and unidentifiable. He soon learnt that it was an American deodoriser, and although he was now accustomed to it, and although it was meant to be a pleasant smell, he still found it slightly nauseating. He knew that people entering the room were confused because it was not the scent of flowers, but so obscure and weird that they might wonder if it was the smell of a decomposing body. Graham thought what strange noses the Americans must have. So the weird odour, the cross, the fake flowers and the velvet drapes enabled this tiny room to be elevated, euphemistically, to a Chapel of Repose. Perhaps, thought Graham, it was still better than what the British thought was acceptable. When they went to see a body at the local mortuary, there were no frills or euphemisms, it was a utilitarian Viewing Room.

Graham would always meet the family and take them into the Chapel of Repose where they would anxiously cluster around the edge of the most expensive box they would ever buy, and then they would peer inside. He often felt sorry for the incontinent corpse, given no choice in the matter and no less abused than the elephant man by all this peering. The word peer assumed a constant gaze, but the term body peepers might be more applicable, people taking a looksee, a glimpse or a glance, as if unable to look death in the face. So little wonder, thought Graham, that the words dead and death were ugly and taboo to the company. They dictated the use of, in repose, and, passed away. They also favoured, passed over to the other side, but that was considered inappropriate in Carlisle; it meant a night out, over the Pennines in Newcastle!

The longer Graham observed the peepers the more convinced he became that what was said was the opposite of what was felt. When a peeper said, doesn't he look comfortable, he knew that it was they themselves who were feeling discomforted. In was in this discomforted state that their vocabulary would become restricted to a mere handful of platitudes and, he or she is at peace now, was easily the most favoured. When they said this, he sensed their underlying stress; it was the contemplation of death. Were they now focussed on the meaning of life, or wondering where the time had gone, and why they had spent so much of it watching East Enders?

Then there were those who turned up and demanded some private time with the deceased; for the door to be shut and for them to be left alone with the corpse. It was often the estranged daughter or the ex-wife, each wanting a final communion with the deceased. Graham often wished he knew what was going on behind the closed doors. Was it an apology, or a begging of forgiveness? Were they damning the dead for dying on them or telling them how they had ruined their lives? Perhaps, they were children with the philosophy of the poet Philip Larkin and his lines, 'They fuck you up, your mum and dad'. Words of love or hate; words, perhaps, that could only be said to their dead face.

It occurred to Graham that it wasn't just that death was stressful in itself; it was because the funeral process hadn't evolved. The modern world was forced backwards into a culture which jarred. People in the past were familiar with funerals and dead bodies, but now many reached retirement before they attended their first funeral or even saw a body. It was a palaver, the silver cane, top hat, hearse, the coffin and now the viewing, and many suspected that the deceased would have been violently opposed to it all, let alone the cost. Graham knew that the only person comfortable in this anachronistic arena was the funeral director.

†

At Flynn's, Brian was having a bad day. Moving the hearse in the yard that morning, one of the drivers had scratched the side of the vehicle on the wall. After a rant, Brian had disguised the damage with the ever ready black enamel spray and with the hearse now pristine, they drove off for their first funeral at a Cumbrian village. At the churchyard, the gravedigger was standing at the graveside and started chatting to Brian; it was the usual gravedigger's lament, "I have arthritis in all me joints, piles, diverticulitis." He paused before adding, "And a hernia." He said this much as a soldier reels off a list of his campaigns. Brian wanted to say, "And you always cut the grave too tight and put me under stress," but deferred, because of the man's age and ailments. A few minutes later, standing beside the grave, and as if anyone had a choice in the matter, the vicar said, "You have picked a lovely day for a burial." He could just as inappropriately have said, "You have picked a lovely day to die," because, at that precise moment, the chief mourner keeled over and fell to the ground. Brian knew instantly that he was dead; he had arrived in a limo but left in an ambulance. There was a spontaneous reshuffle in the status of the mourners, and the graveside service was completed. As Brian left, he felt sure he heard a mourner say, "He would have wanted it that way!"

Brian thought that perhaps the day was looking up; at least he was now certain to have another funeral! Back at the premises, the embalmer had turned up and was at work. Strange, Brian thought, how we still call him the embalmer, which sounded so old fashioned. He never questioned the process, just as long as somebody else did it. It made life much simpler now they were self employed, especially with all those health and safety issues. Formaldehyde wasn't something he wanted his staff to work with anyway. The American embalmers considered the British far too casual over formaldehyde exposure limits.

There was also another issue. If the bereaved thought that the body didn't look like a dead body should, or even if it was completely unrecognisable, then Flynn's could always blame the embalmer. Their relationship with the embalmers wasn't good anyway because they were always whinging that they couldn't do a decent job for the amount the funeral directors paid them.

It occurred to Brian that perhaps thousands of people a year were viewing bodies and quietly saying to themselves, "Perhaps they have got the bodies mixed up!" At least, if the deceased was dressed in their own clothes for viewing, then the eyes were convinced that it was their beloved, even if the brain said otherwise.

Brian wondered what would happen if the EU prohibited the use of formaldehyde, something that they had threatened. The thought drifted away as he went through to the back to see how Em was getting on. The embalmers name was Martin but the name Em had stuck and signified embalming to all the staff. Em had been working for some time on Jack. The body and hair was already washed and the face shaved. As Brian watched, Em was putting in eye caps and a mouth former, to remove the sunken look. But, he decided that the face still looked gaunt so mastic was squeezed into the mouth, and the cheeks puffed up nicely, like a cutesy little hamster. He then packed the throat and nose with cotton gauze. Em looked pleased with himself as he used a few stitches inside the upper and lower lip to close the mouth to what he considered, professionally, to represent a benign expression. This genial look was Em's artistic tour de force; his personal interpretation of dead!

Brian wasn't usually present for the next part of Em's work because he found it less appealing, but decided to stay. Em flexed the arms and legs to relieve the rigor mortis and to encourage the flow of embalming fluid through the blood vessels. He then effortlessly severed a calf tendon to straighten a left leg that refused to lie flat. As Em wielded his scalpel, Brian couldn't help being impressed by his skill, even if it was because he wouldn't do it himself.

Brian stood well back as Em placed a plastic sheet under the body to retain any leaking fluids. A small incision was all that was needed into both the carotid artery and jugular vein in the neck so that tubes could be inserted. One tube ran to the embalming machine, the other to the waste sink. It was strange, thought Brian, that something so macabre could be so fascinating, but he had to stop thinking of Jack as a person in order to continue watching.

As the machine purred, the embalming chemicals flowed in and the blood was forced out. Em told Brian that it had flowed out so easily that Jack was probably on Warfarin before he died. They both knew how difficult it was when the blood was really clotted. Em commented on how brilliant the GEC machine was because it pumped in a couple of gallons in no time at all.

Em occasionally repositioned the limbs to aid circulation. As he watched with a knowing eye, he touched the skin now and then to judge the pressure, and from experience he could see when the embalming was complete. He was always careful, unlike others, who would over pressurise a body with the fluid. It was a bit like radiator anti-freeze, he explained to Brian, and it was always wanting to escape. In the hands of the careless, they knew it could seep through the skin and orifices and into the plastic coffin liner. It would pool there and present a challenge to bearers. If they lifted the coffin out of a low hearse, they could tilt it so much that the fluid spilled over the edge. It would then drip onto their shoulders and sometimes lay a trail along a crematorium or church floor.

Em located his trocar, and inserted the sharp point into the abdominal wall with a neat jabbing action. He guided it under the ribs, to ensure that the tip pierced the heart and lungs to enable any fluid to be sucked out by the machine. With skilled thrusts and lunges of the trocar, the stomach, bladder, bowel and other organs were emptied. For Brian, the amazement was how little damage appeared on the surface of the skin, yet beneath, the razor tip was shredding tissue. Em implied that he was nearly finished with Jack as he sealed the external holes with trocar buttons. As he packed up his equipment, Brian asked him whether the EU were doing anything about them putting the blood and waste down the drains. Em had heard nothing but he didn't see it as a problem anyway.

When Em had left, Brian needed to rid the premises of the smell of the embalming fluid so he switched on the extractor fan and used his usual deodoriser to spray the body.

As he did so, he reprised his role ready for the arrival of Jack's family to view his body. The name is Jack, he kept reminding himself, Jack, Jack, Jack. It was so important to use the familiar name and to get it right. He could hear himself saying to the family, 'Jack is in restful repose; look at Jack, he is so at peace; you will leave today with a beautiful memory picture of Jack.' He is confident his words will give comfort to the bereaved. He is confident that the family will be pleased that Jack had been sanitised.

That evening, Brian settled in front of Border Television, aware that Ben was going to be featured. He was one of a select group of people who had been asked to do a two minute video slot on a subject they were passionate about. So, sure enough, there was Ben, standing by his own natural burial grave, doing a two minute slot called, Video Me. Brian wondered what he was going to say against his profession this time and he didn't have to wonder for long:

"I have just two minutes to talk to you about my eternity resting in this spot", Ben said, standing in front of his own grave. "This is a natural burial grave in Carlisle cemetery. My funeral will take place here, and my burial in grave number 56, already bought by me and ready for the day. It will be an essentially simple funeral, with natural human dignity. No embalming fluid will pollute this body. You see, I know that funeral directors hide embalming behind two false words – hygienic treatment. So, no hygienic treatment and I will be placed in a cardboard coffin. Not for me the pretence of dignity. The oak coffin really made of chipboard, the brass handles really made of plastic. There'll be no false pomp and concern with status at this funeral. My money will go to the living. This body will nurture a tree, one of a forest of trees, all creating the birth of squirrels, wildflowers, owls and other birds. A real memorial, the tree of life. No chunk of stone and epitaph will tell you anything about me. After all, nature knows who I am. I feel it is important to be my own person. I don't want that processed, dull and expensive affair that many people call the modern funeral. I don't think that planning my funeral is macabre, after all, it's too late when I am dead."

"Huh!" said Brian.

CHAPTER FOURTEEN

Dead Good Funerals

Ronson got very annoyed if one of the BALU members referred to him as the godfather, but it happened occasionally. It usually arose if he exhibited signs of criminal intent towards Ben. Others joked that perhaps cadaverfather, or bodyboss might be more to the point. But he wasn't in a light mood, he was feeling too exposed nationally. Other BALU branches were using him as a conduit for news and gossip; there were too many phone calls and too much whinging about Ben. Every time a council opened a natural burial site he would get calls, and in one week, Kettering, Ayr, Bristol and Dudley had all gone that way. Added to this, the DIY funerals were all the rage and it had spread into garden burials. Who would have thought that a body under the patio would have become a garden accessory? Ronson could imagine chicken fat dripping off the barbie onto granny's grave.

As if this was not enough, one of his members had been to see the comedian Donald Scott performing in Carlisle and in his act he had done a skit about seeing Ben at the crem to get himself a cardboard coffin to take home. Ronson did not find this amusing. There was little to smile about when it came to the publicity that Ben and his ideas were attracting; rather than diminishing, it seemed that funerals were always in the news.

Ronson reluctantly accepted that Border Television had found a new celebrity in Ben West; it was only a matter of time before they would be introducing him as their funeral correspondent. Fresh from his Video Me spot, Ben had been featured in the launch of a new book called, The Dead Good Funerals Book, written by two artists from Ulverston in South Cumbria. Then, there he was again, onscreen with another artist and hand painted cardboard coffins and this had been syndicated all over the UK, and generated yet more telephone calls. What the hell was he supposed to do about it? It was not as if the BALU members helped their own cause. Roger had recently presented a talk on funeral directing to nurses at his local Carlisle hospital. At previous talks, the nurses had jokingly commented that he was always dressed in black. No danger of that at his most recent talk; he had appeared dressed as a woman! That got the crack going and didn't improve the reputation of funeral directors. Then it was a close run thing when another funeral director in Carlisle had spent a night in the cells after a domestic disturbance. He was a councillor so the front page of the News & Star had read, 'Councillor spends night in the cells'. The fact that he was a funeral director was, fortunately, buried in the text.

Just when he thought that the publicity had peaked, it erupted again. It was no less than the BBC Countryfile programme; a full five minutes on natural burial in Carlisle Cemetery. Suddenly Ben was in a clique with farmers, and natural burial was the ultimate in farm diversification. Ben had polished his lamp; the genie had leapt out in the form of a farmer. Nobody in their wildest dreams could have envisaged farmers getting into the funeral business. BALU, completely unprepared, saw their closed market gaping wide open to a new threat. Within days, some farmers were on the media and, annoyed that their local funeral directors would not even talk to them, were suggesting that they might bypass them altogether, by collecting the bodies themselves. Ronson wondered if anybody manufactured a tractor in black. He was bewildered. As a Cumbrian he knew country folk. He had friends who would just love to be buried on a farm. They were people whose entire lives were spent with cow shit on their boots and the wind in their faces; the crematorium was, in reality, an alien environment. The telephone rang again, it was a member who had seen the Sunday Express and the Sunday Sun. Its boobs on page three; Ben on page four!

The only light relief was the 'Day of the Dead!' Ronson told the BALU members about it that evening. The moment he said the words, 'Day of the Dead', the derisive laughter had started; then the jesting and quipping began and all semblance of order vanished. It was an event Ben had arranged at Carlisle Cemetery as part of a national day organised by Nicholas Albery from the Natural Death Centre. The idea had been pinched from Mexico; cue for more laughter. Somebody reminded them that people were supposed to take a picnic to the cemetery, presumably so that the deceased could join the party. The mention of Nicholas Albery had then started off a chain of reminiscence about the questionnaire he had sent to funeral directors a few years earlier asking how they would help people wanting to do a DIY funeral. Ronson pulled them back into line, by reminding them that they all ignored the questionnaire and the Natural Death Centre had cited this as evidence that UK funeral directing was – anti consumer! Cue for more laughter. Somebody suggested that asking funeral directors to help people with DIY funerals was like asking turkeys to vote for Christmas; cue for more laughter. It was then that Ronson reminded them that a similar questionnaire sent to councils also drew little response. He closed the meeting by suggesting that they ignore the Day of the Dead. One member thought this rather a shame because it would have been an opportunity to wear his sombrero!

✝

Roger was idly sitting at home, drinking a mug of tea and reading the October Harpers & Queen magazine. This was not his usual choice of reading because it took no interest in manly pursuits like horse and dog racing. His wife had passed it to him, open at page 158, displaying an article called, Vigour Mortis. Roger read, with an air of resignation, 'Attitudes to death are changing, with Aids bringing it closer to the young, and the over seventy fives living longer and longer. As market forces begin to act on the old-fashioned funeral, the deceased has become a consumer, entitled to the send-off of his choice – trad, anarchic, or eco-friendly. Kate Berridge looks at a new kind of death wish.'

Roger found these sorts of articles tiresome, the way they drawled on about the need for death therapists and the urgency of a five minute life review: What did you mean to do with your life? What did you actually do? What were your regrets and what did you rejoice in? Then, to his wife's surprise, he burst into laughter but she could see that he was about to illuminate her. He read from the article, "One therapist enthused about sharing the bed with the deceased: It is really a beautiful thing. You can sleep with the body or watch television with it, an experience that many women may find strangely familiar when the time comes." Roger's wife laughed too, and he enjoyed the fact that they laughed together – until he suspected that he and his wife were laughing for different reasons.

He read on, conscious that he was a bit player in this tale and felt, in equal measure, the excitement of a participant, and the disquiet of what was still to be read. Kate continued, 'If we are seeking more enriching alternatives to the impersonal and perfunctory twenty-minute funeral, we are also becoming more secular'. Roger expected such a magazine to focus on celebrities and, sure enough, there was the back garden burial of Sarah Miles and then Melvyn Bragg interviewing Dennis Potter on television during his terminal illness, the latter swigging morphine and whisky whilst clearly in pain. Roger turned the page and Ben's cemetery was there, under Groovy Graveyards! Roger anticipated that the article would not spare them and, sure enough, the next paragraph read, 'Our embarrassment about death has kept the funeral trade under-cover and unregulated, with a near-monopoly on the 625,000 funerals in the UK each year. Traditionally, the funeral parlour, like the massage parlour, has been the place where nobody wants to be seen – both establishments conducting furtive commercial transactions for the relief of sadness. Like sex, death is a social minefield, which is why we are keen to delegate it to the men in black coats'.

Roger might have laughed but he didn't enjoy the article. The writing was too clever and humorous and he didn't like the way that these movers and shakers were intruding into his world. The phrase, furtive commercial transactions, and then comparing them to some dirty massage parlour, was hurtful. Roger reached for his pen and underlined the bit about the massage parlour to read out at his next BALU meeting.

✝

Ronson didn't like having to analyse or think too deeply so he did what he always did in these circumstances and focussed on the superficial; nothing was more superficial than cardboard. His members were still whinging and constantly reminded him that cardboard was tawdry and vulgar. Others quipped that it was a fuckin' cardboard shoebox. Cardboard was an antagonism, a conflict, a discord. It clashed vilely with the traditional funeral. The top hat and the silver cane could not sell cardboard.

BALU head office was of the opinion that opposition to green initiatives would cast them in a bad light. Ronson recognised this and suggested that it was the weak construction of the cardboard coffins that was the issue because they sag and must be difficult to push into a cremator. Accepting this logic, they agreed to write to Ben's professional Institute and ask them for a statement on the acceptability of cardboard coffins. By return of post they received a copy of the new, Charter for the Bereaved. To their dismay, it gave cardboard coffins the thumbs up; if people wanted one to reduce emissions from cremation and use fewer resources, then they should be allowed to make that decision.

So that was that, thought Ronson, any council who adopted the Charter for the Bereaved would promote – Ben's views! If BALU can't stop this happening then it will mean that the bereaved will be the arbiter of what constitutes a dead good funeral – not the funeral director.

CHAPTER FIFTEEN

Heavenly Hoist

'Heartless Thieves Steal Baby Memorials', was the newspaper headline that morning. Roger scanned it whilst keeping one ear to Terry Wogan's banalities about senior moments. Sure enough, the report included a comment by Ben, on two small marble angels that had flitted from one of his cemeteries. The article was written in the typically heartless thieves and yobbos tone, all about feckless modern youth, but Roger knew that the real story was entirely missed. Why would anybody steal memorials? There's not much call for angels on the black market, unless, that is, they are dressed in fishnet stockings and high heels! Neither was it easy to slip one out, like a contraband mobile phone, from inside the jacket and say, "Fancy an angel; I'll do you a good price?" Roger knew that it was not the kids to blame; it was those bloody white witches again!

It was an age old Cumbrian pastime, this white witchery. They were not the cackling dark witches of Macbeth, but benevolent witches, which might appear an oxymoron. Some people had said to Roger that they were Wicca and he knew how to spell that word because he had once arranged a Wicca funeral. To cast good spells at their rituals they needed some death related symbol, preferably one that had a pseudo religious association. The life-size Italian marble angels might have been preferred but were over two tons apiece, so a mini version was necessary. The bite sized ones, the compact little cherubs, were inadvertently designed with this function in mind. It was an unfortunate coincidence that these were mostly situated on children's graves so the thefts had an even greater touch of insensitivity about them. At least the white witches seem to have an awareness of the distress so only stole from old, unvisited graves. There was an assumption that the parents were dead; unavailable for interview by the press.

What surprised Roger and everybody who knew, was how the purloined cherubim would make a miraculous reappearance about a year later. It was not only undamaged, but a sparkling, pristine white, obviously having been carefully cleaned by some ambrosial fluid; possibly Jif. The miraculous reappearance was always in somebody's front garden, usually a small garden, the cherub carefully placed in the centre of the lawn during the hours of darkness. It was, perhaps, fortunate that none of the gardens belonged to a Catholic, as this would surely have turned the area into a Cumbrian Lourdes. He could imagine big Bernadette, a Cumbrian lass, drawing the curtains one morning to greet this apparition on the front lawn with, "Holy Mary, Mother of Jesus, there's a feckin' angel on the lawn!"

These thefts really annoyed Roger because people who had bought marble angels from him, having read the news report, would immediately telephone him in a nervous tremor, convinced that their angel had been abducted. Once or twice he had felt obliged to visit the grave and subsequently assure them that their seraph was still on guard. It was also obvious that the police were lacking divine guidance as they had never caught the thieving devils. The apprehension of a witch would be a real news scoop in Cumbria; an opportunity for the ducking stool to be brought back into use.

Roger recalled the local cemetery foreman who thought he saw an apparition; it was two young lads pushing a supermarket trolley through the cemetery. He saw them but his brain refuted the vision; this was not Tesco! He followed them and watched as they dug into leaf litter under a massive tree and secreted something from out of the trolley. They walked off with the empty trolley, totally incongruous and yet acting as if they were trundling through the supermarket. The foreman dug under the leaf litter and found two large sacks of Imperial Mints. The hole had mints in, so to speak! The police, when called, thought it was a hoax but on arrival saw not only the sacks but a trail of mints leading off into the distance. One of the sacks must have had a hole in it. The trail was followed, mint by mint, for half a mile until it lead the sleuths to the Penguin sweet factory where they found a hole in the wall of the storeroom. A few questions about kids seen pushing a supermarket trolley, about kids permanently sucking mints, and the two little sweeties were identified.

These dumb kids, thought Roger, they get pinched but the white witches go undetected. Perhaps it was because the witches had the sense to look like all the other virtuous women tending graves, the time honoured widows, and not pathetically conspicuous like the two lads. He recalled one young mother who had regularly taken her child in a pushchair to the crematorium Hall of Remembrance, secreted pot plants and flowers under the covers, and then walked out. Was she taking them for nefarious ceremonies, or was it just mean theft? Did anybody ever check the child in the pushchair; peer in and say, "What a little angel!"

CHAPTER SIXTEEN

Body Blow to Corpse Control

"There's no property in a dead body so you can't own it, you can't own your own body after death." Ronson focussed on this enlightenment from one of BALU's top dogs in London. He vaguely knew all this but had never really understood it. "So will this Dead Citizens Charter put that right?" he asked. "Well" said the Londoner, "I suppose it's a bit of a misnomer because if you are dead you are no longer a citizen. By definition, a citizen needs to be breathing, otherwise he's ours." There was a touch of irony in this comment, and a touch of familiarity between fellow funeral directors at opposite ends of the country. "Semantics aside," he continued, "It would allow people to control what happens to their body after they die." Ronson was puzzled, "But, surely, they can do that already so why another Charter?" "No!" came the reply, "In common law there is no property in a dead body, no one can own it, not even the dead person." Ronson was confused, "But if I die and complete a will, won't my executors follow my instructions?" "Well, it is only a moral obligation to follow your funeral instructions; they are not legally bound to do what you want. The executor or your next of kin can ignore your instructions and do as they wish. It may also be a waste of time because the will is really about your estate, and is often read after the funeral has occurred."

Ronson knew all this, however imperfectly, because he had known funeral instructions to be changed against the wishes of the deceased. This Londoner spoke to him as if he knew nothing, but he was at the coalface. He knew how much worse things were now than they used to be because of all the divorces, live-in partners and stepchildren. Everyone was fighting their own corner so disputes were commonplace. Even simple things like a person's religion could be a dilemma. They started a Catholic, married a Protestant and hadn't seen the inside of a church in forty years. He'd often found himself counselling people to define what they really wanted, popery or the spartan church or chapel. Even these green funerals could cause dissent. The deceased might have wanted a natural burial in a cardboard coffin but other members of the family would let it happen over their dead body! He'd recently been grateful to a distant aunt who had kept the family straight with a shake of the head and a barbed comment about sending them off in a cardboard box. They changed to a conventional coffin. But he still felt uncomfortable when the wishes of the deceased were not followed; it was a matter of trust.

Ronson countered, "So what is the legal status of the person who arranges the funeral then?" "Well," said the Londoner, sounding impressed with his own knowledge, "The next of kin or executor has a legal right to claim possession of the body and there is an assumption that they will arrange a funeral. Otherwise, if the body lies unclaimed then it falls to the local council to pay for its disposal." The word disposal grated on Ronson but he recognised that it was more a concern about bodies lying around and not the niceties of a funeral. "So this Dead Citizens Charter will allow binding instructions to be left by the person who has died?" said

Ronson. "Well, that's the aim but it would require a change in the law. It wants people to be given the right to dictate what happens to their body until it is buried or cremated, which would include any funeral service." Ronson reviewed his myriad of funeral experiences, and then asked, "So if a person left instructions to be buried with a former lover then that would have to occur?" Ronson detected no hint at the other end of the telephone that this was a facetious question. "Yes, the instructions would be assumed to be irreversible."

"So there's a meeting next week about this Dead Citizens Charter?" said Ronson, "And I suppose Ben West will be there?" "Yes, he will be adding his pennyworth because he now manages the Charter for the Bereaved, and if he thinks that it will damage our interests he will definitely be there." Ronson wanted to know why their interests could be damaged and was told that if people dictated what they wanted, there would be much less flexibility for the profession than currently existed. Ronson doubted this. He thought that it was the big companies who were nervous; they suspected that if people left instructions, very few would tell their nearest and dearest to spend, spend, spend. This Dead Citizens Charter was a means of opposing the hard sell.

Ronson changed tack as he wanted to know where the idea had originated from. The Londoner explained that although the Charter was fronted by a Free Church minister, it was thought up by Lord Young of Dartington. His wife had died and he was upset over the way funeral directors had advised him and handled the arrangements. And the Lord said, 'I have this commandment called the Dead Citizens Charter and thou shalt control thy body after death!' "This is what comes from upsetting a Lord, especially a radical one like him," said the

Londoner. BALU would have to tread carefully with the clergy and a Lord involved!

Ronson was aware that BALU had appeared supportive during the initial preparation of the Charter. It was difficult for them to oppose the need for someone to have control over their own body, but then a far more radical clause was inserted; that people should appoint a funeral guardian before they died. It came as a shock, and they all knew that it was to stop a funeral being a crisis purchase. A person would be nominated to procure and manage the funeral; someone who was not emotionally fettered; someone who could dictate terms to the funeral director; someone who could make the funeral a perfunctory purchase.

Ronson and his members had considered this proposal idiotic. Who was this person who was going to be above sales pressure, who was associated with the deceased, but not distressed by their death, and capable of controlling them? It would have to be a friend, or a workmate, perhaps, someone who would keep the distressed widow or widower away from the Funeral Arranger. Ronson scoffed at this; why should they worry, even this person would be inexperienced in arranging funerals and the skilled Funeral Arranger would still be able to run rings around them.

He was confident that this Charter would not see the light of day; he was right. The opposition from BALU focussed on how the funeral guardian's role had the potential to cause massive conflict with the bereaved. It was all that was needed; to Ben's dismay, the Charter proposers threw in the towel. Even BALU was surprised at how easily they capitulated. They had wanted universal acceptance but when the role of the funeral guardian was rejected, rather than modifying the proposal, the whole Charter was sacrificed.

Ronson put the demise of the Charter on the agenda for his next BALU meeting knowing that it would greatly improve his member's humour; it was truly a good death! At the meeting, the banter headed off in all directions but became focussed on how the newspapers would report it. The buoyant mood encouraged members to invent their own headlines – 'Failure To Breathe Life Into Dead Citizens Charter', 'Corpse Charter Breathes Its Last', but ended with the clear favourite, which was Roger's suggestion, 'Body Blow To Corpse Control!'

Ronson stayed on in the bar after the meeting chatting to the locals, all of whom he knew through the funerals he had arranged for them. He prided himself on recalling all the bodies he had handled and actually relating their appearance and form to the surviving children. He could see the deathly noses, chins or hair types replicated in the room, and they spoke to him. One woman, a nose, listened intently to Ronson telling people about the Charter's failure. "Surely", she said, interrupting him, "It's no different to me putting down what I wanted to happen when I had my baby. We all do that now, you know. It was so much better letting everyone know what I wanted." A few heads nodded in agreement.

Everyone Ronson had spoken to about the Charter agreed that with a name like Dead Citizens Charter it was a dead duck from the start. It sounded far too French Revolutionary and about as relevant to Cumbria as ballet. It was a British idea, so why hadn't they called it something straightforward like the Funeral Charter? People might have taken more notice of it if they had.

†

Brian had arranged the funeral and it was slightly unusual

because the man had died on his bike in Italy. Nothing appeared amiss, until that is, the viewing occurred. His parents had seemed very conservative and it was to be a conventional Christian burial. Then his friends and partner arrived and they were all girt in black leathers, with the words, Hell's Angels, prominent across the shoulders, and tattoos across the knuckles. They were uncomfortable; was it words like Chapel of Repose or was it his appearance; he wasn't coffined in his leathers?

The funeral was tense as the parents tried to ignore the bikers and the partner; it was the world that had killed their son. But it was impossible to ignore the deep throb of perhaps a hundred bikes as they chocked up the little cemetery and all of its roadways. It was an intimidating imposition, but ultimately futile as the bikers stood around, unable to bear his coffin or play rock music; they were passive observers as he was committed by aliens! There was no lingering, the family left immediately in the limos and the resigned bikers stood around the open grave to say their farewells. They were deflated by their inertia; the funeral had not celebrated the life of one of their own, a Hell's Angel who had raised huge sums for children's charities; the religion was not his religion. So, they had their own ceremony planned in accordance with his wishes; at least he would be there in spirit. As Brian drove away he reflected on what one of the bikers had said to him, "It's amazing that a man gets to forty five years of age, has a life, and still the parents stick their fuckin' nose in!"

✝

The Funeral Arranger at Roberts's was finding the funeral

123

heavy going; it was a true crisis arrangement, every parent's worst nightmare, arranging their child's funeral. It was a young male road death. The mother makes the arrangements, the father says little. The picture emerged that they had bought their son a zippy car. It was all girls and showing off, but at least this time, none of the passengers were killed.

These funerals were familiar to Graham; it was a rural thing. Indulged kids given a set of unearned wheels and let free in a playground of narrow winding Cumbrian roads and lanes. The game ended when he failed to notice the curving left-hander embellished by a large, immoveable oak. The shrines were now on every road, always on a bend, the innocent tree garlanded in plastic flowers and cards; if not a tree, it was a solid stone wall.

The Funeral Arranger could relax; salesmanship might be considered inappropriate but then it would not be needed. There was no end to what the parents were prepared to spend in the hope that it would assuage the pain of their loss. Or was it their guilt, thought Graham, in not meeting the first duty of a parent, of keeping their child safe from harm? It would be a big funeral, with an ornate coffin, endless flowers, and a large memorial to follow. Every day the parents will visit the grave and clean the wordy inscription in the belief that it will give them solace. The grave will also become a shrine to his mates, which they will be able to cluster around to pay homage; to them, Shaun will become a celebrity and local hero.

Graham could make no sense of it. His training informed him that he was meeting a social need and that he was helping these people. That was too simplistic; was it all just a show, an expensive display to illustrate the depth of their grief, or was he just fuelling their grief? For certain, nobody was innocent anymore.

CHAPTER SEVENTEEN

Lifting the Lid

It was a baby's body – in the cremator! The cremator operator shook himself and re-focussed his gaze through the spyhole. The burning remains of an old woman was what he expected, but there it was too, a baby's body. In panic, he called Ben but by the time he arrived the alarm was over; the gas jets have had no impact. It was a doll! Later, in the ashes, they found the charred ceramic doll in amazingly good condition but, with its haute couture incinerated, it was seen to be a naked mademoiselle. An antique doll, of French origin, that must have had some personal significance to the old woman. Ronson, when he heard this story, knew it reflected durable old stuff. An American Barbie would have lasted two seconds in that heat, then puff. Just like poor Ken, no doubt!

This incident was one of the topics in the latest circular from Ben's office. There was always a whinge or two about funeral directors and on this occasion it was about one of the BALU members allowing a doll to be placed in the coffin. The firm had protested innocence, suggesting that the family had secreted it during a viewing session. Whether true or not, the coffin lid was screwed down over two bodies and nobody thought any more about it. Ronson was annoyed that his members were being criticised for going easy on the bereaved; for not policing their actions.

He'd noted how Ben's circulars always seemed to disproportionately focus on what was in the coffin. This was not, as might be assumed, the body, rather than what accompanied the body, on its journey to the cremator. The concern over what was under the lid did not arise with burial, as anything placed or erroneously left in the coffin was hidden underground. Only a future Time Team would ever know what was in those coffins, but that will be in a few hundred years. With cremation, a glance in the cremator or the guilty item sojourned in the ashes was tangible evidence of somebody's carelessness. There had been hammers, wood planes, screwdrivers and pliers, a golf club, even surgical instruments such as scissors and clamps. These were just the items that would not perish, there were probably many more that burnt without trace.

In the past it was just a chastisable act of carelessness but Ben's recent circulars had elevated the misdemeanour to an environmental catastrophe. Aerosol cans had always exploded in the cremator, historically, a minor bang but Ben now made it sound as if the crematorium roof had blown off. Ronson knew why the problem had worsened; the funeral directors all kept aerosols hidden in the coffin. This could be whipped out and a quick spray would mask any odour just before the bereaved entered the Chapel of Repose. There was nowhere else to store the can and so slipping it inside the coffin was all too easy. Pity, they sometimes forgot to take it out.

Ben took this all too seriously; it wasn't so much the can as what was in the can. The annoying thing, thought Ronson, was that the other crematorium in the area didn't consider it a problem at all. He was confident that they could leave a couple of Kalashnikovs and a hand grenade in the coffin, without a word being said. Ben's last whinge had been about the acrid black smoke caused by plastic shoes put on the deceased. He made it sound as if the sun had been eclipsed over Carlisle that day. It wasn't helped when another of Ronson's members had been asked by a family to dress the deceased in his fishing gear. The idiot complied and struggled for ages to put a pair of thigh length rubber waders on the body. Some say the black smoke eclipsed North Cumbria that day.

The antagonism between Ronson's members and Ben really came to a head when he forced them to stop the long cherished practice of coffin varnishing. Some of the older funeral directors slapped on so many coats of varnish that they could see their reflection in the coffin. They detested Ben for this act but Ronson had accepted the argument after Ben had asked him to witness one of these coffins being charged into the cremator. The varnish had erupted in a great flash; a balloon of black smoke had surged back into the room and swirled around the cremator operator. Then, black smoke and heaven knows what pollution poured out of the stack. Ben agreed with Ronson that it hadn't been a problem in the past when the coffin went into a relatively cool cremator but now, with the new cremators, the coffin could only be charged when it was at eight hundred degrees centigrade. The varnish was now lethal. This couldn't be challenged; Ronson had to accept it and so would his members.

The media hadn't taken any interest until heart pacemakers started blowing up in cremators. Headlines appeared about the pacemaker battery punching a hole in the brickwork; explosions were newsy but black smoke and theoretical pollution did not sell papers. Ben had constantly reminded the funeral directors to ask the widow or widower whether a pacemaker had been fitted, and, if so, that it had been removed by the hospital. This was now routine and although exploding hearts might be a thing of the past, stupid actions were less easy to stop. He'd been at the crematorium on one occasion as the cremator operator raked out the ashes together with reams and reams of paper, much of it unburnt. Perhaps the deceased had been very small, whatever, piles of old telephone directories and newspapers had been packed under the body. The amount of paper was so excessive that even after ninety minutes at eleven hundred degrees centigrade there was little impact on it. Paper from the charred edges floated everywhere and the cremated remains were mixed into a papery mass. Ronson said nothing to the member who was responsible; he considered that Ben's job.

Even Ronson baulked when the cremator operator told him about another funeral director, who was also a jobbing builder. With a load of old glass fibre insulation mat in his yard, he thought it would similarly make ideal packing for raising a body. Immune to the gas jets and temperature, the glass fibre remained in sheets with the human ashes adhered to it. It was difficult to remove this congealed mass from the cremator, and it was a nightmare to sort the ashes out for returning to the bereaved. The danger from the glass fibre to staff had completely bypassed this funeral director's brain. If the body had been completely wrapped in the sheets, it wouldn't have cremated at all.

Ronson finished his breakfast, and headed for the office. It was another of those days on which Ben was the main topic, but not just locally. Councils were beginning to adopt the Charter for the Bereaved and BALU members from branches around the country seemed to think that being on the front line, Ronson was the one to contact. Initially, he felt a touch of pride at this recognition, but too often the caller displayed too much confidence, an arrogance that suggested that they could tell Ronson how to manage the situation. The latest was a cocky sod from Preston who had telephoned him to say that he had just ended a long conversation with Ben and had put him right. Ronson groaned inwardly. He had heard this before. This Lancastrian was deeply upset that Ben had said they were a rip-off during an interview on News at Ten the previous evening. Ronson knew that Ben had not actually used those words but just implied them. The Lancastrian related to him how he had told Ben that he spoke a load of rubbish, only to become incensed when Ben suggested that the mark-up on their coffins might make people think otherwise. What surprised Ronson was how the man said, granted, in reply to Ben's accusation. He did the same when Ben suggested that they never give people written quotations for funerals. Granted, was again his response. Not surprisingly, this Lancastrian then told Ronson that the conversation with Ben was going nowhere so he changed tack by accusing Ben of being left wing. At Ben's denial, he then suggested that he was a member of Greenpeace. It sounded, thought Ronson, more of a compliment than an insult. When Ben had also said no to this accusation, he then stated that he was obviously one of those politically correct people who would not use words like blackboard and chairman.

As if the conversation between Ben and the Lancastrian had not gone badly enough, Ronson now had to be told how, having defined what kind of person he thought Ben was, he felt it necessary to tell him what kind of person, he was. That he was far right and there was no shame in earning £100,000 a year as a good funeral director. Ronson, at this stage, imagined how Ben must have been itching to ask him just what constituted a good funeral director and how that could justify those earnings. But the cocky one, perhaps anticipating such a question, ended the conversation. Ronson was furious when he heard all this but the damage was done. The members, including this idiot, knew the unwritten rule; they must never lift the lid on their earnings!

CHAPTER EIGHTEEN

Flower Power

'Council to Recycle Wreaths' was there, prominent on the street hoardings outside every newsagent. The newspaper editor must have considered it the most inflammatory of his news items for that day. Roger was confident that it would sell a few more papers, bought one himself, and immediately called Ronson to update him. The report came as no surprise to either of them because some months earlier Ben had written to them about the council's intentions. Now it had gone public, Ronson was perplexed that other than Roger, none of the members had contacted him about it. If the members appeared unconcerned then head office certainly wasn't. Their message was uncomplicated; the scheme must fail.

When Ben had first written to them about recycling wreaths there was complete disbelief. It had caused uproar at their BALU meeting. The idea was preposterous, and a letter from Ronson was immediately dispatched to say that BALU considered the idea insensitive and an insult to the dead. He was feeling confident that he had a grip on the issue because he had followed Ben's every move. He knew that he had walked into a florist's shop in Carlisle carrying two old wreaths and wanted to know whether the plastic frames and oasis could be recycled into a new wreath. The florist, initially taken aback, had said that the oasis would have to be binned, but the frames were reusable. When pressed for a price, he had said they were probably worth about a pound each. Ben had, apparently, been pleased to hear this and explained that the council sent about thirty thousand of these frames each year to landfill, which was both expensive and wasteful.

The funeral directors were under no elusion about what Ben thought of wreaths and hothouse flowers; he hated them! The man was completely screwed up. He was always telling people that the millions spent on them could go to charities and other good causes; he completely ignored their value to grieving mourners. Then, he would go green again and point out the air freight miles involved in sending flowers around the globe. Also, the harm caused to women growing them in the Third World, because the chemicals resulted in abortions and abnormal babies. Ronson relished this aspect of Ben; he always went over the top. But Ronson was staggered at Ben's naivety. He seemed unable to recognise the massive marketing machine that was floristry; it was really all about money, not flowers. Didn't he realise that flowers could have a sinister scent? A cemetery manager in Wolverhampton had found this out after he had openly stated that flowers were a waste of money; he had received anonymous telephone death threats.

Despite his confidence, Ronson's intelligence network indicated that the situation was far from clear. The general feeling was that most florists were upset about using recycled wreath frames, but with money involved, would they change their minds? It was no surprise that a firm who sold the frames to florists had telephoned Ronson to register their dissent. But it was his own members that really worried him. Some were holding back, especially those in the Carlisle area. Graham had telephoned him and it was obvious that he anticipated some action from BALU but wanted nothing to do with it. He had made some lame excuse about his managers being worried about adverse publicity.

Ronson knew the real reason why everyone was on edge. It was because youngsters with special needs would be doing Ben's dirty work! They were horticultural trainees managed by Social Services and working in a redundant greenhouse complex in the main cemetery. Ben knew that for their unit to survive, they had to raise the sum of £10,000 every year, a sum they could not achieve by just producing bedding plants for sale. Aware of their struggle to survive, he could see that collecting and stripping the wreaths was ideal work for them and they could then resell the frames back to the florists. Ronson imagined Ben's line of thought: because it was special needs youngsters doing the work, BALU would probably back off.

†

Graham was in and out of the cemetery most days, and he often saw the youngsters working in the greenhouses. There was an open invitation to visit because they were piloting the wreath scheme, so he went in to see what it was all about. The youngsters were all smiles and joking and joshing but it was obvious that it was work they could cope with; they enjoyed having purpose. A pile of old wreaths was loaded onto a small truck and the kids bustled about, dwarfed by their oversized visibility jackets. The talk was all football and Carlisle United; they seemed to have no other conversation. They were immediately intrigued by Graham's formal black clothes but could make no correlation between these and his role as a funeral director. One young lad, with Down's syndrome, repeatedly asked him what he did and he replied but it was an indefinite, repeated refrain. Graham found this really irritating; the question, the answer, the question, the answer. They were noisy and fractious but in the dry and warmth, would spend all day stripping the dead flowers and foliage ready for composting. The oasis was binned and each frame laid out on the greenhouse staging, with far more delicacy than was really necessary, a set distance from its neighbour, ready for a florist to inspect and hopefully buy.

Graham could see the kids were oblivious to the potential discord in what they were doing. The wreaths had no higher purpose, they were just things, and the job was just a job. He knew that he could never work with such kids, that it would try his patience, so he had nothing but admiration for the young supervisors. They were so tolerant in the face of all this tedium. When he talked to the supervisors it was obvious that the wreath scheme had great potential for the unit. One gave away his Cumbrian roots when he said that the lads loved fettling the wreaths but, beneath the casual chat, Graham could sense that they really wanted him to understand how much this work mattered to them.

Graham had a problem because he knew how BALU felt. He could not be seen to support Ben without compromising himself. He knew Ronson, locked away in his little town, would never look in and actually see the kids working. All he cared about was usurping Ben, but this was not about Ben. Regardless, Graham couldn't allow Roberts's to be associated with attacking the scheme so he telephoned Ronson and put himself and Roberts's firmly on the fence.

†

Ronson knew precisely which local florists would not participate in the scheme, but Cumbria and Southern Scotland was a big area. Slowly, florists started to call at the nursery unit and the scheme blossomed. As they bought more and more of the old frames it was easy for the floral snitches to work up a list of those calling at the greenhouses. He knew death threats were inappropriate and he suspected that he could not say it with flowers, so after discussion with Roger, they decided it was time for condolences to be sent!

Ronson had no intention of putting anything on the BALU agenda so he and Roger carefully selected those members they could rely on. So, on a specific day, these hit men were sent to their designated florist; it was a friendly, compassionate visit, to show concern for their business, and rumour of their concern would quickly spread to other florists. If a condolence card had been sent, it would have said, 'With deepest sympathy over the recent loss of all wreath orders from your friendly local funeral director'.

Ben, wreathed in success, was stemmed overnight. The scheme stopped instantly. No florists visited the nursery or put in orders. The wreath frames piled up, the youngster's work wilted, the income withered. Ben was a virgin in the floral industry and Ronson glowed as reports filtered in of his deflowering.

Ronson kept BALU head office updated and they coordinated by issuing a press release which was picked up by the tabloid press. He was surprised at how cleverly it sidestepped any reference to the work of the special needs youngsters. It focussed on the insensitivity of the idea, on Ben

West, a jobsworth, who took people's wreaths. The national tabloid press loved all this and implied that Ben must be on the take by posing the question, 'and for whose financial benefit was the scheme proposed?'

Ronson heard little but good news; the scheme was destroyed and Ben was tarnished. If BALU feared repercussions then they feared needlessly. Ben's union took up his case confirming that he had been libelled in the press but advising that legal action would be too expensive to contemplate. Ronson was euphoric; but he resisted the urge to send Ben a condolence card!

CHAPTER NINETEEN

Girl Power

Above the gate, the Victorian clock face marked time; but for whom? It suddenly struck her as so odd; the face looked into the grounds, staring at those for whom time had no meaning. Was it for people going to funerals, or even staff waiting for funerals, people who could not afford a timepiece? She watched the terminal time tick, and more importantly, watched the gate from her spot secreted in a grove of conifers. The notice board had told her what to expect, and, sure enough, at ten minutes to eight a van drew up and a fair haired man closed and locked the gates. Content, she was now the only human alive inside. She walked, crossing the murmuring beck, to the plantation of young oak trees. Looking east and, framing the trees, she could see what she knew were the Pennines, rounded bluish mounds now the world was closing down. Two bats, pipistrelles, she was sure, suddenly appeared and flitted between the young oaks and she blessed their movement and vitality; the manic and insane desire to exist. As she walked to the trees she had considered where to sit, and the banks of the beck had seemed most promising. She walked slowly in that direction and, reaching the beck, turned left along the bank. Off the path, the lawns felt soft, as if carpeted in moss and not grass at all. She realised her sensory powers were awakening as her vision was denied light. The blind, she thought, would feel these mossy lawns through their shoes.

She had to take care because old memorials stood out of the grass here and there, some so small that they could be fallen over. They were all decrepit in this area, there were no signs of the graves being visited; it was not a place for people. It amused her, the human world had moved on but the natural world simply didn't care.

She finally settled on a lush grassy bank, between bushes, a few feet above the beck and within sight of a small footbridge. The morning light would illuminate her spot to any passing walker. She sat and took some time to nestle into a neat recess between the tussocks. She was warm, wrapped up against the chill evening air. It was so quiet, yet the silence was a cacophony of night sounds. There was an occasional light breeze in the trees and leaves rustled. There was movement everywhere, not least in the long grass on the beck banks, and she made out a hedgehog dragged by its snout seeking food. The beck tinkled intermittently, not consistently, as water passed around some impediment she could not see. A tawny owl called and its partner answered; she knew they knew an interloper was present; not just a human but a live human. Were they calling her? She had never before felt this calm.

Now settled, she mulled over the time; what time was right and why did time matter anyway? She settled on midnight, it seemed appropriate, a new day and a new start. It gave her time to muse over her family, over events. There had been a sequence to her life and it was inevitable that it all lead to this one spot, this spot in the grass. She checked and was reassured; the plastic bag was in her left pocket. She had no worries; she had packed a second bag inside her jacket, just in case!

✝

He grabbed the News and Star the moment it dropped on the hall floor, already anticipating the front page; the graphic headline, 'Woman Commits Suicide in Cemetery.' Roger knew it was all about Joan Wood but he read the story just the same. Everybody had some measure of the tale but the details were vague and confusing. How did a woman living in France come to die, to commit suicide, in Carlisle? Why did she do it; and why in a cemetery? Did Ben know any more than the papers and would he say anything to Roger even if he did? These were the questions he was asking himself when he went to see Ben. If he expected reticence then he was wrong; Joan Wood had wanted her story to be told. So Ben, though still in a state of shock, had no hesitation in telling Roger all that he knew.

Ben's first contact with her had been some two years earlier, when an envelope arrived from Paris, incompletely addressed to, 'Manager, Green Burial Site, Carlisle, UK'. It contained a letter which said that she had heard Ben talking about green burial on the BBC World Service. She immediately knew that she wanted a green burial but there was a problem; Carlisle was the only location in the world. Ben told Roger how he had written back stressing that following her death in France, the transport of her body and funeral in Carlisle would be expensive. Thinking that this was the last he would hear from her, he had been surprised when she replied immediately, insisting that there would be no

139

problem because she would die in the UK. Even more surprisingly, that she enclosed the remittance for a natural burial grave. She was, at that time, only the eighth person to buy a grave so she was given number WB8.

Ben then related how on the previous Friday, two years after she had purchased the grave, she had made an appointment to see him. She didn't mention that she owned a grave and neither would she tell his staff why she wanted to see him, so they had warned him to expect a complaint. In fact, he was surprised to find her a formidable ally because she opened the meeting with strident, yet supportive, comments; cremation was polluting; mowing graves was wasteful and memorials were futile. She then grilled Ben over green burial; what trees and shrubs would be planted; were the trees of local provenance; would herbicides be used; how was it to be managed; what would it look like in one hundred years; what indicator species would be attracted to the site in the early years? It soon became obvious to Ben that her knowledge was considerable and far ranging. But it wasn't just this that impressed him; she seemed fearless about death. She said that the body was just an envelope, the spirit a separate existence. She even felt that there was no death because our atoms went on; we just changed form and were perpetual. Roger asked Ben whether she appeared religious but he said that she didn't express views either way. But, she definitely had a philosophy; a return to nature.

Satisfied with Ben's answers, she said that she intended to walk to the natural burial plot on her own. She did this, and Ben saw her walk out of the cemetery later that afternoon. He was later aware that she had been staying in a B & B in Carlisle.

Roger said that he had heard that Ian, one of the gravediggers, had found her body when he had patrolled the cemetery on the Sunday morning. Ben explained that Ian was pretty upset. It was a shock and he had said that he didn't expect to see anyone dead in the cemetery, not on top of the ground anyway! He found her sitting upright, nestled in the tussocks, staring from within a plastic bag. Ian called the police and the coroner had taken over her body. Roger asked Ben if he knew why she had committed suicide in the cemetery and he told him of a letter found in her clothing. It said that she loved the natural burial idea, explained that she already owned a grave and then described her funeral wishes and gave contact details of her daughter in Devon. She finished off by suggesting that Ben could tell people her story, about how committed she was to this new way.

Ben told Roger that the daughter had already visited the mortuary to confirm that it was her mother. She had then called on him, concerned that he might be upset. She told him that she was not surprised over what had happened; her mother had always made it clear that she would stay in control, and end her life once her health deteriorated. She was adamant that she would never enter a hospital, or nursing home, and put herself into other people's hands.

But Joan had left another surprise for Ben, and it arrived in Tuesday's post; it was a letter from the other side! On Saturday afternoon, in between a full breakfast and an evening dinner in her Carlisle digs, a matter of hours before her last walk to the cemetery, Joan had written letters to Ben and her daughter. Ben passed the letter to Roger:

Dear Mr. West,
I must apologise for not being frank with you but I couldn't tell you really who I was and why I am here, could

I? I must be one of your first customers since we spoke and wrote just after your BBC broadcast and I have your receipt for my natural burial which I am sending to my daughter. Your cemetery is quite the loveliest I've ever seen. I spent some peaceful hours wandering around it yesterday. I found the natural burial area. What a lovely site with the view of the moors on the skyline!

In case you haven't come across me when you receive this, my remains are probably close to the stream by one of your bridges. I'm quite of sound mind – not depressed or bothered by worries. It's just that at 75 and with a dodgy heart, this way I shall be neither a burden to my family nor the state and my grandchildren can inherit all I've worked hard for all my life. Congratulations on your being the pioneer of this absolutely right way of disposing of our bodies, which after all are only our discarded envelopes.

Will be back soon!

Joan Wood

Will be back soon, made Roger smile. There was a confidence in it that made biblical resurrection seem almost childish. Roger asked Ben what he thought would have happened if she hadn't liked his response to the grilling? Would she still be alive? There was no answer.

Subsequently, Roger found that the cemetery staff had said the same thing as the many people who spoke to him about Joan's action. The stock response was, I could never do that. It was society, it had created a death process that deliberately avoided any ripples on the surface; people had to die quietly, out of sight and under sedation. But Joan blew this conspiracy apart; there was more challenge from her death than he had seen in thousands of funerals. Roger kept thinking about her last few hours. Did she smile when she prepared the plastic bags to take with her, overwritten in large print with the words, 'danger – plastic bags can cause suffocation!'

Roger saw the difficulty; Joan Wood, the suicidal environmentalist, had to be labelled eccentric so that society could disassociate itself from her. Otherwise, her pragmatism and her honesty were just too challenging. He heard over the next few days that she had tried to get Plymouth Council to create a natural burial scheme and, when that failed, had visited a new site at Brighton, but was dismissive due to the poor response to her questions. So this woman in her seventies had been an activist, not just in life but in death. It was all this mother earth stuff.

Roger was not surprised that Ben was seen as the ferryman for environmentalists but, as with most news stories, it quickly blew over. Joan was, after all, an offcomer and her action was too in your face and somehow not Cumbrian, it didn't belong. Her funeral took place quietly, and as she had requested in the letter found on her body, with Ben and his staff acting as bearers using a basic cardboard coffin. There was to be no ceremony and no one else to be present. That included her daughter, who was expected to visit some time in the future. Roger wondered what the coroner's report would say. It was something that he knew was bothering Ben, who was having to submit his version of the event and was desperate to avoid that fateful line at the inquest; that she died whilst the balance of her mind was disturbed.

A few days later Roger was telephoned by a press agency. It was a death hunter, a man seeking his opinion, as a local funeral director, on Joan's death, for an article he was preparing to sell on to press agencies. Roger detested these people and calmly said that he had no comment. He knew that it would not be written sympathetically; it would be sensationalised, probably ghoulish.

The Joan saga reminded Roger that women dominate life as well as funerals; they have the finger on mortality's pulse. He carried on ignoring his wife's concern about his increasing weight and poor health, but he knew full well that she was the survivor. But it didn't bother him because the enduring female physiology was only appealing if it came with good health. Going on and on, year after year, without any real quality of life, little more than just breathing, was, to him, vile. Joan knew that too, and she had the answer. He compared her with the feeble men, the infuriating sods who, as soon as they knew what he did, like parrots, repeated the refrain, "They can just put me in a black plastic bin bag and throw me over the wall!" He had yet to do one of those funerals!

Later that afternoon, Roger was back up at the cemetery to inter a casket of cremated remains and Joan is superseded by Rosemary in his thoughts. Roger had never heard of Rosemary. He was surprised to be told that Rosemary was for Remembrance. He dipped his fingers into the tray of herbal shards and the aroma was strong and rich. As he handed the tray back to Ben, he realised that this was his idea; to offer Rosemary leaves instead of soil for the committal part of the burial ceremony. Roger immediately saw its appeal, but he knew that Rosemary was far too middle class; she was fine for chefs but he dealt with common or garden cooks. His clients were not into herbs any more than he was; nobody cooked with them let alone sprinkled them down a grave. It took his mind just minutes to come up with an alternative; his widows would just love to strew a red rose down the grave, the passionate farewell; much better than herbs or wet filthy soil. He felt this was a stroke of genius. Red roses and tears; perfect!

Roger suddenly realised that Ben was sometimes right. He was rabbiting on telling Roger that far too many burials of cremated remains were poorly done, without ritual or ceremony. Ben recounted some of the miserable arrangements made by other funeral directors, taking care to exclude Roger's firm. He was dismissive of many of the younger funeral directors, who seemed to be embarrassed by ritual, and, unlike Roger, didn't know how to deal with people. They always appeared rushed, wanting to get it over with, just shoving the casket down the hole without ceremony; that he knew of pets that had had a better burial.

The talking stopped as the widow and family walked towards them, and Roger greeted them. He casually chatted to avoid any sign of haste. When ready, he nodded to Ben, who walked forward carrying the casket of cremated remains on a red velvet pad; they followed him to the small grave where the casket, on its velvet pad, was placed beside the open grave. Roger asked the widow whether she would like to lower the casket, but she volunteered her daughter. Roger quietly told the daughter that this was her final act for her father, putting his ashes back to the good soil and eternal peace. She took the white ribbons attached to the casket with trembling hands, lifted and lowered the casket into the grave; she quietly shed tears that glistened on the surface of the oak casket beneath her. Roger shed a professional tear. Then, they all stood around as Ben read a short secular service, always the one that Roger liked because it contained his favourite poems; knowing no appropriate poetry the family always agree. As the words drifted over this now sacred spot, Roger held out the tray so that the widow, and then the daughter, could sprinkle Rosemary over the casket. Roger told them that Rosemary was for remembrance but, in his mind, had already substituted the herb with roses. He enjoyed these little secular services in his role as master of ceremonies, relaxed without the formality of a minister, the cemetery staff reading what he thought appropriate for his family. He knew he did it well, with a touch of flair and emotion. Ben was right; the young funeral directors were useless.

But it was not as straightforward as Roger thought. He hadn't expected to be challenged by roses. The first widow that he approached clearly thought that it was an established ritual, and he was not going to tell her otherwise. She liked the idea and he had then confirmed that there would be twenty close mourners, so he instructed his staff to buy twenty long stemmed red roses. Now, he was staring at one of his gnomes, ill at ease cradling the roses and unsure how to hold them. He knew that other funeral directors and cemetery staff called his aged male bearers, gnomes. It was a fact that they were always on the short side. Roger had given them strict instructions on what to do with the roses but their actions appeared unpolished; ritual needed belief and confidence. At the end of the service the gnome passed a rose to each of the twenty mourners, but Roger noted that it was too quick, too urgent. Then, the mourners, especially the principal ones, cherished the rose and seemed reluctant to cast it down onto the coffin. So he had to bid them to do it, to say that it was their last earthly token to their Mam. It was with artistic licence that he reminded them that roses were for love, and remembrance!

On the drive back the gnome spoke, which was unusual. "Did you notice the men, boss?" "No," said Roger. "They was really uncomfortable holding their rose, hid it behind their back, some of 'em. And when they threw it in the grave, they was really embarrassed." Roger discounted the comments; the women were enchanted and that was all that mattered.

Roger glowed when he thought of these touches; even his wife had said how many more compliments they were receiving from their families. He put these thoughts aside as he considered an unusual problem. He was dealing with a double death where a widower had died just a few days after his wife. At first sight it appeared melodramatic, a dreamily romantic end to the couple's lifetime idyll. They would be interred together to cement this lifelong union, so devoted that the man dies of shock when told of his wife's death. The reality, Roger knew, was rather less prosaic. The two old crocks had been jostling each other for years over who would be the first to go. Each day might have been a bonus, but they were so drugged up by medication that it was difficult for them to be sure they were having a day. With the first hint of comprehension, they held a daily drugs conference; who takes what and when. Each drug had a certain merit and, given an opportunity, they would reel them off, as if each was an award for sterling service to everlasting life. The funereal problem, as it were, was far more mundane. The children were naturally upset, not so much about the deaths, but about the question of decency; rather less to do with the bible and rather more to do with the Karma Sutra. Is it right for the mother to go down the grave first, and the husband to go on top? Roger appreciated that this was a reverse missionary position long since abandoned by the couple. After long discussion, punctuated with long silences, the family finally agreed for dad to go down first, and mum to go on top.

After the couple were interred, or as one of the staff said, were duly mounted, Roger headed back to his own car. Walking towards him was a tall, attractive young woman in cream tights and high heels. He was struck by the sheer vivacity, the flamboyance, of this encounter after an hour with the solemnity of mourners. She passed him going in the opposite direction; he stopped, looked around and stared at the retreating and excessively pert backside; something was not quite right. The walk was too jaunty! He resumed his perambulation conscious himself of avoiding a feminine lilt, only to see Ben hurrying towards him with his swift masculine stride. He is in pursuit of somebody they have christened the cemetery flasher; someone who wonders around naked on warm days. Roger turned and walked alongside Ben, but was soon breathing hard with the effort. They reached the road junction, but too late. The lady boy was down the side drive, running at full pelt, her high heels waving in his hands. He was soon into the trees and disappeared. This was the young man who, weather permitting, lazed naked on the cemetery lawns, taking his cue, as it were, from the monumental erections all around him!

Back at the office, Joan and Rosemary and roses were quickly put to the back of his mind. No sooner did one woman's newsworthiness diminish than another rose to prominence; but this was a woman used to notoriety, one of Roger's least favourite women – Maggie! And it was not because of politics that she was today's news topic, not directly anyway. It was because she had involuntarily taken centre stage at Carlisle Council's firework's show. Every year the show became more and more spectacular and this year a Mancunian arts group had been given the job of outdoing the previous year. About twenty thousand people were gathered when, immediately prior to lighting the bonfire, to a great fanfare, a cross-dressed guy, a lady guy, was brought out and paraded shoulder high around the arena. She was then mounted on top of the huge bonfire by several hairy youths, no doubt each with a degree in media studies! A massive cheer reverberated around the crowd. Clearly seen on guy's chest was the word, Maggie, and a sign in her hand said, 'Fuck Maggie'! Unlike Maggie, this lady guy was clearly for turning. Fingers of fire were inserted and the blaze started; Maggie was cremated. Today, the sparks were really flying. Complaints had poured into the council, and a national media frenzy was taking place. But after the television news finished, there she was, Maggie Thatcher, large as life, canvassing. The slogan behind her was far more boring than at her cremation – 'Don't just hope for a new life – vote for one'.

The next day, at breakfast, he picked up the Saga magazine, the one that magically knew when he had turned fifty and started dropping through his letter box. On the front cover was another of those infuriating seventy year old women, who look forty, were having sex at least four times a week and hadn't a wrinkle to be seen. They repulsed him. It brought to mind Joan Wood, and he balanced her against these women, who were always so vain and vacuous. He could imagine them on their death bed, with their last gurgling croak of expiring breath. They would, no doubt, say, 'Don't I look good for my age!'

After flitting through the magazine, he organised his staff for the day. A daily routine that, he believed, disabused people of the fact that his wife was really in charge, and then he headed off to the crem. There were just three mourners present, a well dressed woman and two old men. For Roger, it was the all too familiar. The minister droned through a service he had heard a thousand times. Then, the unfamiliar happened; the woman stood up and left the chapel. It was not just a purposeful walk, but a walk with evident stress; he could see a physical urgency to be out of the chapel quickly. As if this were not unfamiliar enough, the vicar suspended his monotonous verbiage and said, with purposeful clarity, "We must ignore that departure, I regret that she is from the coddled South East and she cannot face death!" Not all women can hack it, thought Roger.

CHAPTER TWENTY

Hell's Angels Wheelie in Heaven

Graham was talking to Phil, a funeral director and builder, as they waited to start a BALU meeting. Phil was telling him about the funeral of a motorcyclist, who was considered a madman by locals because they could hear his sports bike screaming up and down their Lakeland valley most days of the year. This young man had loved the Lake District, not, as is usual, for its scenery or walking, but because of its resemblance to the Isle of Man TT course. So, it was inevitable that the sinuous death ride would claim him, his warm blood destined to stain red the lichen growing over the stone in a wall on a sharp bend. Phil, having scraped up the gory mass, mixed with slivers of chippings, soil, grass and fragments of green slate, was aware that the valley could return to its bucolic tranquillity, the sound of bleating sheep no longer obscured by decibels manufactured in Osaka. To Graham and Phil such deaths were now commonplace and unremarkable, rarely even making the local papers. For Phil to even mention it was an indication that it had a touch of distinction.

The motorcyclist, or rather the remains of the motorcyclist, had been cremated at Carlisle. Weeks later, his biker pals gathered on the summit of Castle Crag to scatter his ashes, a familiar occurrence. Thousands of ashes scattered this way, the perpetrators unaware that this simple act of love, seemingly innocent, was fundamentally changing the soil and the plants of the Lake District. Every BALU member was aware that the National Trust had declared war on the practice. Even their staff, the ones who emptied litter bins, were distressed at handling so many empty cremated remains containers; still with the deceased's name attached! What was worse, they were all plastic polytainers, as the trade called them, and unrecyclable.

What was an uncommon occurrence was that the bikers took it upon themselves to excavate a large hole at the bottom of this ancient fell, beneath towering pines. Into this pseudo grave, with much ceremony, they interred the mangled bike. This mash of metallic technology, now silenced, was covered in soil, and the shovel placed just below the surface. What was in the minds of these young, leathered angels? Was it the resurrection, when their mate would come down from the mountain and dig up the bike? The Cumbrian inhabitants of the serendipitous cottages would know nothing of his return, until they heard the screaming Kawasaki. They would probably think that it was just another idiot on a motorbike.

Graham was really surprised at how Phil, the stolid funeral director, was so scathing of this religion of the Kawasaki. "It's bloody stupid," he said, "They dream of some fanciful motorcycling paradise!" Graham wanted to smile but he couldn't show it on his face; it was as if Phil believed that the Garden of Eden was a real place and theirs somehow a mere fantasy.

Graham sensed that the saga had not ended when Phil said that the lad's girlfriend went on to live his life on her Japanese motorbike. Graham then had this image of a female screaming banshee, which he knew to be mythically right. Sadly, this banshee was no less mortal than her lover. About a year later, blinded by the sun, she too had a fatal crash. Her family, either through spiritual indifference, or detestation of the entire sorry mess, arranged for Phil to inter her remains in a local churchyard and not, as she had wanted, on top of Castle Crag. She would never, in the eyes of the bikers, ride ghostly pillion down the vale. Graham and Phil, experts on death, realised that there were further complications, known to few. That one banshee lies in consecrated ground, the other on a secular mountain crag. A dual resurrection was impossible; they were trapped in parallel worlds! Their spiritual aspirations were thwarted by an earthly technicality; they were destined never to reunite.

Graham listened but was mortally sick of motorcycle deaths and mutilated young bodies. He then took Phil through a motorcyclist funeral he had arranged. The young lad had moved out of the family home because of a grievance with his mother. Remarkably, he did something rarer than Cumbrian hens' teeth; he completed a will and made his girlfriend his executor. Had he a premonition of his death, or was he just a realist, aware of the statistics for motorcyclists; an exciting, rhythmically noisy, but short life? Whatever the reason, it was the girlfriend who contacted Graham and arranged the funeral the dead lad wanted, which included interring his cremated remains in a small grave. The mother sniped throughout the arrangements, but the girlfriend has the law on her side. The mother then demanded a headstone on the grave but the girlfriend, as the grave owner, refused. Convinced that a mother must be able to usurp this stripling of an executor, she headed off to a solicitor. Expensive letters were sent, crafted around the biological need, simply because her legal position was otherwise hopeless. It was to no avail.

Graham related how the girlfriend, not unusually after a death, had headed off to see a medium in Brampton. Perhaps picking up the spirit of the mother, the medium ignored motorbikes and said, "I see vultures all about you!" Both funeral directors burst out laughing, knowing that the nearest vultures were in the arid mountains of warm Spain, not in the bleak, cold Pennines of Brampton. Phil suggested that she probably did not know her birds; that she really saw jet black ravens, the British harbinger of death. But Graham was reflecting on their discussion; the practicable thing of parents hanging on to their children, of children taking mortal risks. Added to this was the age old spiritual thing, where paradise still exists and mythical vultures still intrude. They would have continued talking but Ronson called them, and the other members, back to the reality of the impending meeting. Phil said to Graham, "I think that mythical creature Ben is on the agenda again!"

CHAPTER TWENTY ONE

Peelers Peeling Off

Roger was at the mortuary where Fred, the principal mortuary technician, helped him move a body from the fridge to the ambulance. It wasn't really an ambulance; just a black van and Fred always told Roger how pretentious it was to call it otherwise. He said the same to all the funeral directors but nobody listened. Roger palmed him a gratuity. He knew Fred well and liked him, he was a man who backed up and supported funeral directors. He was in the club, so to speak, and Roger felt relaxed in his company. As evidence of their comradeship, only months earlier Fred had asked Roger to join him when he instructed trainee police officers on postmortem technique, and he asked Roger whether he could briefly explain the role of a funeral director. This was the only occasion where Roger had seen a postmortem from start to finish.

Fred, like many in the death profession, saw himself as a comic and raconteur. And, as with the embalmers, there was more concern with status than was apparent on the surface. He felt it necessary to put barriers, distance as it were, between his role and that of the funeral director; he did not want to be a pariah! Although he handled bodies, he rarely met the bereaved or had anything to do with funerals. As his function was to identify the cause of death, he naturally adopted the medical profession as his bedfellows and mimicked a fine line. He couldn't be a doctor because his patients were dead! He also had to take care not to offend the man who supervised him, the pathologist. So he occupied this rather vague role, part way between two professions. To exaggerate his skill, he took every opportunity to satirise doctors as incompetent. The very fact that they sent the body to the mortuary because they couldn't identify the cause of death did not help their cause.

Roger knew that the system was bizarre. The reality was that these doctors often suspected the cause of death but just lacked confidence in what they knew, so asked for a postmortem. The other side of the coin was that a careless or even criminal doctor, like Shipman, deviously confident in their cause of death, would never refer to the coroner or ask for a postmortem. Unlike other countries, in Britain there were no random postmortems that might uncover criminal acts or negligence.

Roger found Fred's adoption of medical speak rather comical. It reminded him of a pal who did garden jobbing. By memorising a dozen Latin botanical names, in the eyes of garden owners, he could only have trained at Kew! As with this gardener pal, people were impressed by Fred's usage of highfalutin medical words. He picked these up from the pathologist and it was amazing what he could recall. In truth, it was rather like giving the tree its Latin name; it worked insofar as there was nobody around who knew otherwise. As Fred went to work in a suit and ran an aged Audi, appearances were good. People meeting him at the mortuary knew nothing of his lowly salary, or that he dwelt in a purchased council house rather than a detached house in one of the affluent villages around Carlisle. Roger, though, was aware of one weakness in this impersonation; Fred's belief that the rich had to be conspicuous with their wealth. Fred was never seen without a fake Rolex and always wore a gold neck chain and, often, a bracelet. They were always made of that showy, glistening gold, not the matt, expensive stuff. Fred knew that the funeral directors referred to him as Dr. Death! He took it as a compliment.

He also took it as a compliment that, like today, the police sent their rookie trainees to him to experience a postmortem and specifically how it related to a crime. As they trooped into the mortuary, Fred held court and appeared in white surgical overalls, mask and gloves. He started by reminding them that a very small proportion of his work was involved with crime. Only a fifth of all deaths were reported to the coroner, either because the person had not been seeing a doctor before they died, or because the cause of death was uncertain.

Roger doubted Fred had ever been trained as a speaker, but he had developed his own unique style. He would, very confidently, open the session by recounting his stock doctor jokes, intended to relax the young trainees. Roger felt he prepared them rather like a farmer preparing foie gras, the act of stuffing food into geese unaware of the deceit implicit in the seeming care for the ignorant creatures. "Let me tell you about the notes I have received from doctors to illustrate what I have to contend with," he would say. "One doctor actually wrote that the patient refused an autopsy. Another stated, in complete innocence, that the patient had no past history of suicide." Someone in the room tittered. "You can understand," said Fred, "When they write notes like this, why my role might be a valuable one. I could feel depressed about such comments but that simply reminds me of another doctor's note, which said that his patient had been depressed ever since she began seeing him in 1990. Then there's the one who wrote that his patient had had no rigors or shaking chills, but her husband stated that she was very hot in bed last night! Had that been true, of course, it's very likely that it was the husband who had died, one stroke too many, so to speak." Roger knew that this was Fred's lead-in to his long list of Viagra jokes and, sure enough, he said, "Last week I had an eighty six year old man, died whilst under the effects of Viagra. I had to turn him sideways to get him in the fridge."

Roger could see some trainees laughing nervously because, unlike the geese, they were blessed with perception; they feared what was coming. Their nervousness increased when Fred's assistant wheeled in a bier bearing the item many of them dreaded, the corpse. There was no doubting it because it was imposing its morbid profile through a thin, white cotton sheet. Fred and his assistant deftly slid the body onto the mortuary table, and Fred explained how the blood had already been drained away via a sluice. Then, with Tommy Cooper flair, he whipped the sheet off the male corpse, just like that! Sure enough, the prop, the ghastly white cadaver, was there, the first dead body the majority of the trainees had ever seen. Their angst was much worst because there were visible aspects they did not expect to see. One was the colour and texture of the subcutaneous fat layer, obvious along the lines of the incisions already evident on the corpse. It looked nauseating, like some form of human butter, but the yellow had a weird tinge. Roger knew that the trainees wanted the body to look benign, but it's not co-operating!

Roger wondered what was going through their minds. Were they imagining a mother, a father, or a partner on the table, or even themselves? Was it this that was distressing, the reason why previous trainees have had to withdraw? None left this time. Perhaps they were the lucky ones, those who could blot out unpleasant images. Roger wondered why this aspect of death was such a psychological challenge to most people, not just these trainees. How many of them will look at their prostrate naked partners in bed later that evening and be suddenly aware of the fragility of life?

Fred then showed them how he carefully checked the external skin for lesions, bruising and signs of drug usage. "This is a body I prepared this morning", he said. Other than Fred, Roger is the only one in the room who realised what prepared really meant. He couldn't saw through the ribs and skull whilst the students were present; the blood would spatter and the body reek as it warmed. Now, he showed them how he used a scalpel; an artist at work. The gloved hand had a slightly peculiar and exaggerated flourish, as if he had interpreted this action as specific to years studying in a medical school. He was, as a Gilbert and Sullivan rendition might declare, the very image of an expert pathologist. He explained how the chest was first opened and then proceeded to turn the skin back, and remove the previously severed rib cage. Fred slyly glanced at the trainees, some looked white and distant, others interested and keen. The tallest of the trainees, knowing the ground was a long way off, decided to retreat, and sat down. Fred pointed out the various organs and the abnormalities of size or position that he might consider. To prove the point, he removed the heart and lungs in one piece, and then the liver and other organs, before carefully replacing them.

Fred was about to move to the skull, but hesitated. He

knew that the fear factor with a corpse was at its greatest with the face. Other parts of the body could be mutilated but the face was sacrosanct. He then explained how he avoided damage to the face by cutting from ear to ear across the base of the scalp; he peeled the skin from behind the scalp and over the face, to reveal the skull. As he did this, two more trainees peeled away to sit down and Fred's assistant, prepared for the mother role, showed some concern. Others positioned themselves to improve their view. As if to challenge them, Fred removed the top of the skull to show how he had previously cut this with a surgical saw; another trainee retreated. Roger saw that these trainees now understood what those in the death industry experience, what death was really about; the bloody, smelly part. The odour got stronger, an odour difficult to describe but undoubtedly organic; the slow, almost anonymous, decomposition of flesh and blood.

The trainees might have expected the session to end at that point, but, with this case, Fred had a pseudo pathologist's plum denouement, ready and waiting, just for them. He asked the trainees what they thought was the cause of death. Like the goose farmer, he had deliberately slipped them little morsels as he had proceeded over what might have killed this man. Some of the trainees suggested a cause or causes, but he parried these and built a certain tension in the room. At the height of this tension, he embraced the shoulders of the corpse and expertly turned it over; near the centre of the back was what could only be a stab wound!

There were mild exclamations of shock, because the majority of the trainees knew that there had been a local stabbing, so it was no great surprise. This focus on a crime introduced a touch of levity, as they forgot the corpse and its dissection, and returned to policing. Fred's performance was given a round of applause. Roger looked at the trainees as they clapped, knowing that they would remember this experience. A few would even remember the jokes, but for perhaps one or two, the experience will have been profound. It will have raised demons and they, most likely, would quit the police force and remove themselves from any exposure to death.

After the session, Roger supped a mug of tea in Fred's bothy, and studied him as he sat opposite. They both despised the system but never said so; a system where the pathologist should be present to check the body externally and to supervise the postmortem, but actually left it all to Fred. Where, for the pathologist's convenience, Fred prepared the bodies the day before, even though he shouldn't. It enabled the pathologist to visit the following morning, and after a brief discussion, and a cursory look at the body, to sign the certificates and leave. For very little work, he got paid by the body, but spent most of his time working elsewhere on other pathology work and teaching students. It was at least three chunky salaries and, as part of the establishment, he was in the genuine Rolex league. The establishment liked to give it a fancy name like postmortem or autopsy, but it was just a perfunctory routine, a time honoured waste. Roger and Fred knew that it looked the part but it informed nobody, and had never exposed a doctor who had committed a crime. Roger looked at Fred and saw a man who was a bit player to the main actors, the pathologist and coroner. It was all a performance!

As Roger drove back to the office he felt for his families. It was the innocent ones, those who experienced a sudden death or had a doctor struggling with his skills, and they were coerced into agreeing to a postmortem. It was just an expensive box ticking exercise. An exercise that would simply confirm what the family and the doctor already suspected. The other cases, where negligent drug overdose might be commonplace, or a crime was being obscured, were just ignored. The doctors could choose whether to police themselves – or not. Roger knew that if the family suspected the pointlessness of it all, and what a postmortem was really like, they would see if differently; some, like him, would see it as barbarous bureaucracy!

CHAPTER TWENTY TWO

Heavenly Snort

"At least his friends were caring, they found a wheelchair and pushed him into A & E; it's a pity he was already dead!" This comment from a mourner did not relieve Roger's cynicism, as he recalled that the man's druggie mates then ran off. Now, he was looking at perhaps two hundred people attending his funeral, including no doubt, his druggie rescuers. Roger knew that the police were out of sight, but were observing everybody assembled; no doubt everybody at the funeral knew this too. The police, when Roger spoke to them at similar funerals, seem to revel in the fact that they could identify just about all the local drug dealers, the cars they drove and where they did their business. Yet he felt an acute frustration that, even with all this knowledge, nothing changed; the dealers dealt and the lads died. It was never girls! He had asked the police why so many deaths seemed to occur in a place like Carlisle, because it seemed worse than in the larger cities like Newcastle. Their stock answer was that the poor youth of Carlisle, farm fodder, as they would say, were so unsophisticated in their use of drugs that they repeatedly overdosed. This was said to him as a statement of fact and devoid of any sentiment. To the police, it was ignorant hedonism beyond the influence of the authorities. These rural lads had always got tanked up on Saturday nights. Now, they got tanked up and took drugs, so what's changed?

Roger detested these funerals; he hated the cant, the pious platitudes of parents and friends. The lad was loved by everybody, he could do no wrong. He saw the guilt lying beneath the sentiments on the wreath cards, he was a bit of a lad, a real character, a star; he was even God's favourite. Deep down, they knew that good lads didn't die like this but they couldn't face words like irresponsible or incompetent.

These funerals were pure anarchy compared to traditional funerals, the kids unaware of the conventions and familiar only with funerals on East Enders. Young girls swarmed everywhere, constantly moving, all crying and some screaming. Then small phalanxes of schoolmates would form groups and huddle together weeping; boys with boys; girls with girls. Tissues sodden with tears would be strewn all over the ground. Roger knew that there was a conspiracy to ensure that parents, indeed, that all adults, were excluded from their juvenile rituals, they had to be exclusive. Like dumb voyeurs from another world, Roger stood with his bearers, with Ben's staff and the vicar, all repelled by this alien drug culture but unable to touch the kids physically or emotionally.

Roger kept his views to himself; vast sums were spent on garish flowers, no expense was spared; these were very profitable funerals. But the drug world had had an even more profound impact on him over the past few months. It had been responsible for the ruin and possibly the death of a local GP. He was a GP that Roger liked, others he was not so keen on, especially those who seemed too concerned with the money for signing cremation forms. He knew every local GP because his firm collected cremation forms from all the surgeries. This doctor defined himself by his willingness to accept drug addicts on his list when all other doctors refused them. Because of the Easter break, he had issued extra prescriptions of methadone to a number of addicts to cover the holiday, and this kid had overdosed and died.

This imperfect system had failed in the past, but on this occasion somebody complained to the police, who were sitting on a national tinderbox with the name of Dr. Harold Shipman written on it. They had to be seen to respond; it was the classic knee jerk reaction. The establishment turned on one of its own; they were pitiless! The doctor was questioned for twelve miserable hours, and this lead to his suspension from work. The media was rampant and the implication was clear; there was a mass murderer in Carlisle. Roger, knowing this conscientious doctor, could not believe what was happening. The police seemed to be paranoid, the drug scene was no longer rural humdrum; here was something very rare in Carlisle, the opportunity for national prominence.

The body would have to be exhumed for further tests. The police contacted the Coroner for an exhumation order and they called in a team of experts from Manchester. This was the team who had completed all the exhumations for the Shipman case, so they knew their stuff. They also had long term security clearance and were otherwise known to the police; they were members of the club. This exhumation was too important to be trusted to Ben's gravedigging staff, the ones who had routinely completed exhumations.

Roger initially knew none of this and was shocked when he was contacted by the police, the more so when he found out that the mother of the boy had been given the opportunity to attend the exhumation. Surprisingly, she had accepted and asked if Roger, her funeral director, could be there with her. So this was how Roger found himself, at dawn, standing at the graveside with a bereaved mother and Ben's deputy, Thelma. The site was surrounded by screens so that nobody could see what was taking place. It wasn't long before two men arrived in a white transit van; it was the expert exhumation team from Manchester! The cemetery staff had part excavated the grave the previous day so it was easy work for the team to remove the remaining foot of soil. The chipboard veneered coffin was exposed. The surface was covered in mud and the space between it and the grave walls filled with stinking water.

The nameplate was wiped clean so that the name could be read out to the police. The experts then proceeded to remove the coffin screws, obviously intent on removing the lid. Roger was aware that Thelma was uneasy. She had anticipated that the coffin would be removed intact, with the body inside, so why was the lid being removed? The cemetery staff always tried to keep the coffin in one piece so that the body was untouched. She assumed this to be vital here as it was now a crime case; surely it was essential not to corrupt the evidence. The coffin lid was lifted out and put aside.

The boys leaden face looked out, straight up through the grave, to leaden Cumbrian skies. Roger was troubled to see that the body was lying in water, pooled inside the coffin. This could not escape through the impermeable plastic coffin liner. To Roger, he looked little different to when he had put him in the coffin. Was it the water acting as a preservative or was it the effect of taking drugs year in, year out? The very wet, and possibly slimy, corpse, lay there as if it were directly challenging the humans above, at least those tasked with its physical removal. Roger was aware that bodies found in the river were the devil to remove, their skin often sliding off when touched. Savouring the challenge, the expert white van man dropped into the grave and stood knee deep in the water straddling the coffin. Was he incompetent? He had obviously brought no Wellingtons, and his ankle boots disappeared under an offensive slop. Undeterred, and to Thelma's horror, he stooped, put his arms under the boy's body, and scooped him with ease out of the coffin.

Roger was enraptured; what would he give for a camera? It was a divine pieta scene, one to be treasured by all Catholics! The white van man, a burly course Mancunian, mimicked the Virgin Mary, the boy, like Jesus cradled in his arms, was as white as marble, his body soft and limp.

He retained this image, but for mere seconds; the smell was too intrusive. Then, it occurred to him that the real Italian pieta was always dry, the clothes neatly draped, but here the wet clothes clung and the stinking water dripped off the body. The Virgin Mary's hairy arms and tattoos shattered the image and he was once again a burly Northerner, with stubble and a pot belly.

The exhumation expert, mister white van man, dumped the boy's body on the graveside turf. To everyone, other than Thelma and Roger, this was the definitive way to conduct an exhumation; these people were, after all, the experts! The police immediately clicked into investigatory mode and the boy's clothing was searched. What, wondered Roger, were they expecting to find? It was surely not the small packet of white powder nestling in the left pocket of his jacket. The senior police officer was not expecting an answer when he exclaimed, "Where the hell did he get that from?" There was a short silence before the person least expected to reply, spoke out. In a clear voice, the boy's mother said, "I gave it to him as my parting present to take to heaven. I put it there when I last saw him at Roger's funeral parlour."

The exhumation had affected everyone, but in different ways. To Roger and Thelma it was an exercise in how not to do an exhumation. As for the mother, she said no more. Her loving present, of a heavenly snort, had been consigned to the hereafter, yet was exposed by a cruel turn of events. She and the police watched as the body was taken off for detailed examination, and both were anticipating the prosecution of the doctor.

The decisions, such as they were, took place behind closed doors. After a trial by media, the threat of multiple exhumations, comparisons with Shipman and the suspension of a doctor, nothing happened. There was complete silence! No case was brought, no apology issued and it was deliberately allowed to lapse into obscurity. The innocent doctor was destroyed and the stress may have contributed to his death from ill health a short time later. Roger was saddened that a true account of what had really happened would never be found in the Cumbrian archives.

CHAPTER TWENTY THREE

Say it with Cards

The Teletubbies had a lot to answer for! The tiny tots took their televisual cue and granddad had to have a helium balloon on his grave; the grandchildren oblivious to the fact that he was dead. The balloons bobbed in the breeze, each spiked to the turf or tied around a headstone. Graham mused over this fact as he walked along the rows of lawn graves. His mind bounced from kiddie TV to considerations of harmony; the various wind chimes on graves tinkled without accord and they all clashed with the chattering windmills frenetically capturing the wind, and bobbing balloons. It was a modern symphony, the music of plastic tat, as the funeral professionals liked to call it. The prohibition of plastic tat was a war cry all over the country as purists demanded that councils and churches ban everything not considered aesthetic. Decent people did not place this stuff on graves; they didn't inscribe mam or pop on gravestones.

It fascinated him, this conflict. He knew Roger loved plastic tat because his families loved it, the ones from council houses. Graham detested it because his customers at Roberts's were more discerning. This was the reason why so many of his customers went for cremation; because the lawn graves were cluttered with so much tat. He knew Ben's opinion on it. He was ambivalent, inclined to think of it as a plastic wave, like detritus swept up on the beach. The wave flowed with the newly bereaved and as time passed, with the decline in grave visits, it would ebb and the detritus become less evident. Even Graham had noticed that those who demanded that inscriptions be restricted to conventional words like mother and father were generally staid Christians. They were not people who would name their son Darren or Sean. No doubt they were aware that the Church of England had banned all colloquial language in churchyard inscriptions, making the vicar a reluctant arbitrator. But Graham was glad he was unrestricted in the cemetery. Not days before a gay man had asked him to inscribe a memorial with, 'Miss you Minx', on his partner's grave. The headstone was a granite heart split right down the middle; a broken heart!

He walked along the grave lines surveying the memorabilia, a word he preferred for the personal tokens left on graves. As Kenny Everett would say, it was all in the best possible taste! There were birthday cards; the deceased was eighty today, but not in a position to blow out his candles. How many more birthday cards would he get? If they still visited in forty years, could they even get a card that stated, '120 Today'? Then, there was a cheery card that introduced a new grandchild, and it even included a photograph of his dimpled, smiley face. It was a child never to be hugged by granddad. Further along the row of graves, a card proclaimed, 'We have moved', but the dead recipient was unable to change their address book. In fact, he wondered whether the granddad's name had been erased from the family's address book following the death. The card suggested that he had just moved so they had changed his address to grave number P65, Carlisle Cemetery; his place in the family unaffected. There were always a small number of cards, or even letters, intensively handwritten; often a long diatribe. In the early days, Graham used to read some of them but now he knew they were always about some personal or family crisis. It was intense and highly emotional yet left for all and sundry to read. He'd decided that many were not so much a message to the deceased, as a message to other people expected to visit the grave. It was mostly a young girl's sentiment, all about guilt and regret. The things they had intended to express, but didn't, and then the person had died precipitately, the opportunity lost. He knew that many grave visitors saw these emotional expressions and immediately destroyed them. Families!

He found the memorial he was seeking. It was small and tasteful, with a short, curt inscription. The family had complained about a mark on the stone, which they thought was a fault. He glanced at it, all that was needed to confirm that it was a rust mark. He knew that someone will have leaned a Christmas wreath against the stone face, and the wires, rusting in the rain, will have stained the stone. It was nature's unwanted memorabilia, evidence that everything perpetually changed. He would suggest Jif and a little water, but he knew it would fail to remove the mark.

As he walked back to the car he noticed smashed ceramic photographs on two adjacent headstones, a third one only a short distance away. The press had featured them only a few days ago under the headlines of, 'Heartless Vandals'. It's strange, thought Graham, how you can say it in Britain with cards but not with ceramic photographs. Only the ceramic photographs were damaged on this occasion and it was obvious that they were targeted; a case of considerate vandalism! Experienced, he now realised that some people really despised these ceramic photos of the deceased on memorials. Perhaps they were the ones who immediately called them, without any prompting, Italian photographs. Was it just anti-Catholic sentiment? People would occasionally comment that it was not very British, suggesting that they were considered ostentatious, or even sinister, foreign icons. The police would take no real interest in the damage even though these vandals were not kids, childlike maybe, but almost certainly aged, respectable people. It was something the British preferred to ignore; the nether regions of society.

✝

Ronson supped his tea and cocked an ear to Radio Cumbria. It was his favourite radio presenter, Ben! This morning, he was being interviewed about a Church of England ruling. They would not allow memorials in their churchyards to be inscribed with colloquial words like mum, dad, or granddad. It was vintage Ben talking about his little death world and soon he was punning when he said, "It's quite upsetting for families because the word dad is familiar and loved by people; it also avoids confusion with the Father!" He referred to the Church's ruling as heartless and quickly emphasised that cemetery authorities, like Carlisle Council, did not do this. In fact, he reminded listeners that they actually encouraged interesting inscriptions, the kind that brought out the essence of the person and had meaning. He considered that this ruling would make inscriptions banal. Ronson laughed and in that gesture, dismissed Ben as an irrelevance.

Ronson thought little about the ruling, but was surprised

at how many people spoke to him about it; if it wasn't that then it was the repainting of the scout hut. He realised that it was these seemingly insignificant issues that interested people. They had probably all read the Daily Mail that morning, which was having a field day on this ecclesiastical dictate from on high. And, of course, who better to approach than Ben? Ronson knew that this was his forte, the short sharp comment, and it kept him in the local news. Only days before he had heard his bearers at Carlisle Crematorium joshing with each other. One of them had read a letter in the paper complimenting Ben and his initiatives, and the others were laughing, but Ronson had missed the point. He had to ask, as nonchalantly as he could, what had been quoted, and was told it said, Going West with West is best!

†

Roger didn't like all the focus on memorials and inscriptions. Another so called expert had even called them greetings cards in the press and this was intended to be an insult. It was the forlorn cry of elitism, something only the British could do. What was the harm? If people were willing to pay, why shouldn't they have whatever they wanted?

He was in the cemetery seeking a grave. The daughters had asked him to give a price for the regilding of mam's grave; there it was, Lily. Roger had no trouble selling the gilded inscriptions because people loved them, but he knew their weakness; they quickly faded and needed redoing after perhaps five years, and it was expensive. Only a few decades ago hardly a soul considered gold lettering; leaded inscriptions were the thing to have but now lead was poisonous. And people used to be frugal with words but the classic 'R.I.P' or 'At Rest' no longer cut the mustard. Now, when they composed an inscription, they recalled the lines penned by grandson Darren at school and they had to be included. One pound sixty per letter seemed cheap, but only to those who couldn't count. He quickly assessed how many letters and figures were in this inscription and it came to three hundred and forty five so the bill would be over five hundred pounds and then VAT on top.

He looked at an adjacent memorial with its artistic illustration of a Foden truck, the deceased driver taking a nap six feet below. Then, in the next row was a picture of a steam train and he recalled that the deceased had driven the last Royal Train from Carlisle to Scotland. Nearby was the dentist, 'Now filling his last cavity'. He liked this individuality, the pictures, the gilding, and the lengthy eulogy. Recent years had added a wide choice of bright stones from China and India. Okay, so they were a bit garish but nobody could afford Portland Stone and Aberdeen granite anymore. It was grave bling but so what! It annoyed him that Ben, as usual, went over the top on these memorials, claiming that the stone was cheap only because of exploitation; that it was quarried by poor families, including their children, working under appalling conditions.

As he looked over the memorials it brought to mind Ben's latest circular to all the funeral directors. A survey had been carried out to see how long the bereaved continued to visit a grave. It showed that people would visit consistently for the first five years, and then it fell away to a tiny proportion at the end of fifteen years. Roger knew that he would never tell his families any of this because they believed that they would visit for ever. He didn't have to read between the lines to realise that Ben was really saying that after just fifteen years, most memorials were abandoned. Roger saw the results of all this every time he went into the older parts of the cemetery. The council's efforts to keep memorials upright, and safe, were expensive because few of the grave owners would take responsibility and pay the bill. Admittedly, many were dead, but their heirs still didn't want to know. Now, Ben was telling them that the council would no longer accept this scenario because it was unfair on council taxpayers. Roger would not mention any of this to his families and he was pretty certain that none of the other funeral directors or monumental masons would mention it either. They just sold memorials, what happened to them after that was somebody else's problem.

He returned to his car on the cemetery drive where he admired the double width memorial positioned on the corner. People were always intrigued when they saw this gleaming black granite memorial, but few actually noticed that it had no inscription. The owners, a couple, had pre-purchased two adjacent graves and had purposely chosen this prominent position. Every funeral coming up the drive passed this spot and it was the couples intention to give them a show; the Chelsea Flower Show! Across the top half of the seven foot wide memorial was the Garden of Paradise. Not exactly the one from heaven, unless it also had electric water pumps! But it was the couple's notion of paradise, with fountains, trees, bedding plants, and all inside a surrounding wall. The garden was immaculate but devoid of birds or any form of life. It would need a large team of immortal gardeners, thought Roger, and he imagined them in their bothy somewhere offstage, supping ambrosia from mugs. Roger loved this memorial because it was just about as far as you could go in the opposite direction to one of Ben's natural burials.

Roger recalled that the couple were over the moon when they first saw their memorial and they would occasionally visit the cemetery to admire it. He knew that they might live another twenty or thirty years, by which time, the picture colours will have faded and they would be in touch with him; they would need a quote to repaint paradise!

CHAPTER TWENTY FOUR

Lardy Arse

This man is dark; every night he sleeps with the grim reaper! Brian smiled as he recalled this comment, an inebriated friend's assessment of him at the pub. A short while earlier there had been ribaldry over past girlfriends. Somebody had said that Brian was different to the rest of them; he preferred his women to play dead in bed! He was aware that because of his job he couldn't help it if his view of the world was a bit perverse. This all came to the fore as he listened the next morning to the Breakfast News presenter declaring that people were now living longer than at any time in the past. He recognised how the presenter immediately buoyed up his voice with this seemingly good news; there could hardly be a listener who felt that this was anything but an advance for mankind. Was he the only one who wanted to complain to the BBC? Didn't they realise that for some people, it wasn't good news?

This perversity was his bedfellow, day and night, due to the daily humdrum of funerals. It was all those survivors shocked by mortality, the reality that life was often pathetically short and meaningless. Daily, he heard the same profound statements, that the death was so unexpected, that he was so fit and that he never went to the doctors. He had two pat answers, neither of which he could express. One was, that if he had gone to the doctors he might still be alive, and the other was, for God's sake, he was ninety three!

The news that morning was really about the baby-boomers, the first generation to experience the Faustian blessing of long life. They had watched their working week decline and this, said the experts, would continue ad infinitum. In the new millennium, the presenter cheerfully stated, people were going to have a life of leisure, retiring early on big pensions and be the healthiest aged population, ever! Brian, the professor, took a perverse view. He saw a mass of octogenarians ready for leisure all right, but it was what Brian preferred to call ultimate leisure!

But this morning the news touched on a new and growing topic; obesity. Brian tried, God how he tried, to stop looking at fat people and immediately seeing a funeral, but he failed. To him, a fat person was the walking dead! He knew that a fat body was not just an inconvenience; it killed them years before their time.

Brian was not the only one to be thinking about the impact of obesity. Ben had also been aware of it for some time and had written to the men in black to warn them about the problems that increasing obesity was going to give them. Only recently a local man had died in an upstairs flat and, too big to be carried down the stairs, the fire brigade had to remove an upstairs window and slide his coffin down a ladder. At the mortuary he topped the scales at forty stone, their maximum, so nobody knew what he really weighed. He needed a special coffin and this was too wide for the cremator. He had wanted cremation but had to be buried. The biers couldn't bear his weight. A grave had to be located beside a cemetery road because a battalion of bearers could hardly lift the coffin.

Ben had coined a word for this new obese generation – burger-boomers! It had started with MacDonald's in 1980 and, if they lived no more than the predicted forty to fifty years, then the profession could all be confident of an increase in funerals from 2020 onwards. Their shorter lives would neatly coincide with the deaths of the baby-boomers.

The combined mass, the burger-baby-boomers, gave Brian a real problem. When this topic was mentioned he could hardly look gleeful, but, deep down, there was this sense of security; it was as if somebody from above really cared! Even if the deaths were in the future, their morbid promise would increase the value of his firm. He knew that there was nothing to compare with this other than, perhaps, a pandemic!

At this point in time, Brian could do nothing in preparation. He listened sympathetically to Terry Wogan fighting the flab, aware that to have any real effect he should have associated fat, not with diet but with death. That might work. Brian discounted, at this stage, approaching the fire brigade for quotes to remove massive bodies from upstairs rooms; they would be based on weight, with additions for sinuous staircases. He made a note to contact the local coffin manufacturer to see whether they had considered the effect of the dramatically increasing BMI; it would sound impressive, if nothing else. He then wondered whether he needed a new approach to fees; to charge by the stone. A lardy arse rate, perhaps!

CHAPTER TWENTY FIVE

Grave Matters

There were four men pulling on sisal webbing and two others wielding long iron bars. He could smell the coffin being exhumed long before he saw it, but as he walked up to the graveside the sodden mass of rotting chipboard was all too obvious. The base of the grave around the coffin was covered in an oozing mass of water, silt and body fluids leaking from the coffin joints. These had split after just three months of burial. Graham was annoyed that he had given Ben, who was supervising, the opportunity to see what rubbish these expensive chipboard coffins really were. But he was also upset because the error was not his; it was with his Funeral Arranger. Not only had the family asked for a grave on the Catholic plot, they had booked a full Catholic service. Even so, the grave details given by Roberts's to the cemetery office requested a nondenominational plot, and that is where the burial ended up.

The term, laid to rest, was unseemly to this family. He was buried amongst foe, the grave ringed by Church of England adherents, Methodists, Mormons and their antithesis; atheists and Humanists. Although each might abhor their neighbour's convictions, they were unified in one instance; they were all papal abominators!

Why had the family taken so long to realise the error? They had, after all, attended the grave for many weeks before the absence of the typical accoutrements of Catholic graves had struck them. Graham had discussed this with Ben, and they both wondered why, if they could spot Catholic graves a mile off, why couldn't these Catholics? Why did they lack any sense of place? When, they wondered, did the family realise that Bernadette's tacky souvenirs from Lourdes were missing from the adjacent graves. Those little lumps of Chinese stone, embossed with the French Saint or the blue robed, plaster figures of the Madonna, that constantly crack and fracture through the miracle of frosts. Why hadn't they missed the plastic flowers so beloved by Catholics? Why hadn't they noticed at dusk the absence of saintly candles and night lights blazing, or worse, that pathetic alternative, the solar lights stuck in a row, and retailed by the blessed firm of B & Q? Where were the angelic host, the marble angels, each with the right index finger pointing to heaven? This assuredly confident finger suggesting that the deceased had skipped Dante's hell and purgatory, and gone direct to a celestial level.

It appeared to Graham that the family may never have noticed, were it not for the grave deeds sent from Ben's office, informing them that what they had bought was, nondenominational! The word nondenominational had a hint of purgatory about it, a state of suspension or none being. At first, Graham thought he might convince them that it was merely a word, but no! They couldn't tolerate their loved one being interred next to somebody from the Church of England, one of Henry the eighths heretics. As a consequence, the Reformation proved expensive for Roberts's because they had to instruct Ben to obtain an exhumation licence and move the body, transfiguring it from the realm of the Tudors and back into the arms of the pope. Roberts's had to foot the bill.

Graham looked at Ben, standing near the edge of the grave. He knew that he would take this job seriously but his thoughts would be errant. He was an atheist and had little time for religious intolerance. He also had an acute sense of the ridiculous, and these religious sensitivities passed him by. Graham looked down at the coffin, which was close to complete collapse, but Ben's staff were skilful. They were able to slip bars underneath the coffin and ease it up a fraction, breaking the suction of the mud. Then two gravediggers dropped into the grave and slid webbing under and around the coffin to hold it together. When the coffin was raised about a foot, they punctured the plastic coffin liner with a bar and the stinking water around the body streamed out of the head end and into the base of the grave. This made it easier to lift intact onto the back of a small truck, at which time everybody breathed a sigh of relief. Graham looked at the gravediggers, their disposable overalls now covered in filthy slime. It was also on their faces, a squirt of body matter from an ill-used shovel, and on their boots and tools. It was not pleasant work and they would all recall the odour for days, even in bed.

None of the family had wanted to witness the actual work, but later that day, the daughter of the deceased met Graham on the Catholic plot; all was now well. After she had left, Graham meandered back to his car doing what he always did in cemeteries, he read the memorial inscriptions. He noted the inscribed RIP on many memorials and sensed the irony; no peace for the one dug up that morning! Rarely, somebody taking a dislike to an abbreviated RIP had inscribed the full Latin inscription; requiescat in pace. This puzzled him because so few people knew what the Latin words meant. Was it a smart ass funeral director or mason giving advice, or was it just one-upmanship by the bereaved?

When Graham went into funeral directing he had expected the funeral world to be mundane, even boring, but he had been surprised by the challenges posed by the work. Only a few months before, he was directing a funeral and it was 11a.m. precisely, at the grave side, and the deceased's son suddenly stopped the funeral service, shouting out that it was the wrong grave. The man looked close to a state of collapse as Graham and the minister helped him to one side, whilst the mourners were returned to their vehicles. The coffin, now in limbo, was returned to the hearse. It was not immediately obvious what the problem was, and the son became aggressive and difficult as a family squabble developed. Slowly, Graham realised that the family owned several graves and this son was now certain that he had shown the wrong grave deed to Graham's staff; he knew the fault was his. Graham spoke to Ben and arrangements were made to excavate the correct grave. The funeral was able to take place the same day but it was not the end of the matter. The son's aggression simmered, perhaps because the error was blown out of all proportion by other family members. Over many weeks, he quizzed Graham as well as the staff in the cemetery office. He wanted to blame either party, but could not find any evidence that the mistake was anything but his own.

Graham mused over these less pleasant aspects of the work as he stood at another graveside later that day. Whilst the coffin was sitting on the putlogs, prior to being lowered into the grave, and the prayers were being spoken by the priest, a robin flew onto the spoil heap, and then onto the coffin. Time stood still! This impromptu interloper was accorded total reverence and Graham could see nothing but delight on the faces of the mourners. Something spiritual had occurred; a robin had sat on the coffin. It was this aspect of funerals that amazed Graham, the fact that, even in this modern world a robin was still a portent. The ancient spiritual world still existed and a robin must be a good omen. Far be it from him to be the iconoclast; to break this image. The reality was far more mundane, the robin sought out the gravediggers every day knowing that the first riven sods bore rich rewards, worms and insects; the grave was the robin's natural habitat.

Perhaps it was no more than a warning of rain, as within minutes it poured down. Graham's phobia erupted, the one where clean shoes and shiny limousines were pure obsession. Within minutes, the funeral experience turned downright uncomfortable. The rain came down like stair rods, the burial service effectively spoiled by all the discomfiture. Graham held a brolly over the chief mourner whilst Ben did likewise to shelter the priest reading his lines. The priest then sprinkled holy water, which immediately diffused as it mingled with secular rain drops, and soaked the shoes of Ben and Graham. The priest's service book flopped with wetness and the saturated mourners had an even deeper air of sadness. Graham knew they would all head off immediately, not stopping to talk for even a few minutes. There was something so essentially British about these funerals; a life ending damply in the dour North.

Only days before, Graham had chatted to Ben after a wet graveside experience, the two of them like drowned rats. Ben did what he always did on these occasions, he suggested that they should erect portable shelters, like the Americans do, but it never happened. It was as if it was the British way, a wet burial; as if decomposition began in the misty clouds! Did burial advocates think that shelters somehow cheated on the experience, that they were only for foreign softies? For certain, Ben was unable to get anybody enthused about spending money buying graveside shelters, and it never happened. Perhaps those involved felt that if inclement weather was a problem then they should choose cremation. For Graham, there were times when a warm, dry, crematorium chapel had a certain appeal.

Graham wouldn't admit it but he enjoyed tapping Ben's brains about what was going on in the business, and so he asked him about a recent Radio Cumbria report on the emerging Aids deaths in the area. With Aids being a terminal illness, those near to death were leaving London and the large cities to quietly die in the provinces. What they didn't realise was the fear they created in rural communities, that they would be contagious long after death. Graham and Ben knew that the fear was itself like a contagion. So, when a young man died down the coast in Whitehaven, the council officers demanded that his coffin be encased in concrete. They both despaired at how empathy was so easily overwhelmed by ignorance.

They were about to leave when the cemetery supervisor, Steve, came running towards them. He looked drawn and white, as if he had seen a corpse. He had! He had just found a man's body in the wooded part of the cemetery with a large tree branch lying across his legs. He had stared at the lifeless, blue face and then recoiled; had he been killed by the branch falling off the tree above? It was a tree that he should have inspected for safety. He felt distraught but immediately called the police on his mobile. But a dead man in the cemetery had to be a hoax call and, as no police arrived, he had headed off to find Ben.

As Steve recounted this story to Ben and Graham, two panda cars were approaching up the main drive. Within minutes, there were almost more pandas in the cemetery than memorials. The scenario was that the man's wife had followed him into the cemetery and, on seeing what she thought was his body, had been too horrified to approach. She had immediately run to the cemetery office, where the staff had contacted the police to say, for a second time, that a man appeared to be dead in the cemetery. This time, they took it seriously.

The police radios told the story in numerous short calls; the man was alive less than two hours previously, he lived just across the road and kept his wood burner stoked up on purloined cemetery wood falling from trees. People often saw him dragging huge branches across the main road to his house. On learning from his wife that he had a heart condition the case was quickly solved. There was obviously a fine balance between the size of the branch and the effort required to drag it home and on this occasion, it was too much. The joy of foraging that had started with manageable kindling had escalated; it was a case of matter over mind.

†

Brian recalled the older funeral directors whinging on about how funerals had changed. In the past they just did the funeral, it was uncomplicated because nobody expected or wanted anyone to know anything about them, especially not the intimate personal details. But now people seemed to take a pride in family rows and tensions, they were everywhere. So, here he was, managing a burial of cremated remains, and feeling nervous throughout the ceremony, unable to relax. He should not have to feel this way. As he watched the casket being lowered into the grave, he scanned the cemetery for the presence of an older woman, but was relieved that no other woman could be seen. At the graveside, the widow of the deceased truck driver, thanked him and moved away. She hated her mother-in-law and the onus had been put on Brian to ensure that the ceremony was kept secret, with only a select few invited. Brian suspected that the mother-in-law would assume that his ashes were placed in the crematorium Garden of Remembrance. Sooner or later she would make enquiries and he could imagine the hurt when she did find out; it was more bad blood. He looked at the wreaths and one had the word Scania prominently written across the front, which was the man's favourite truck. No wreath was allowed to be there from a loving mother, that's for sure. He looked around, attentive, not able to leave the graveside until everyone else had gone. He hated being part of this subterfuge and would now have to dread a phone call from the rejected mother-in-law.

Brian anticipated that his funeral that afternoon was not going to make him any less anxious. It was a sixteen year old boy, a passenger in a stolen car which then crashed into another vehicle. As the passenger, he was crushed to death, his buddy, the driver, was injured but was now mobile in a neck brace. Two innocent women in the oncoming vehicle were also killed. After making all the funeral arrangements and meeting various family members, he knew enough to have written a book about the boy.

The funerals of young people always attracted large numbers and when he arrived at the cemetery, he reckoned that there were between four and five hundred people present. There was an air of menace because the family of the dead boy was blaming the driver, and his family, for the death. The police, anticipating trouble, watched from a distance, not wanting to intrude in private grief. Brian noticed a number of swarthy men in leather jackets standing next to their souped-up cars, their statement of rank. All around, there were young, loud women, some in black dresses trimmed with lace; it was like a scene from an opera! The mourners were the bit parts, repelled by death and yet impelled towards the grave, where Brian found himself hemmed in as the families jostled for position. The tension increased as the funeral service proceeded, and then the mother suddenly turned her back on Catholic ritual, eyeballed the driver, and screamed out "He killed my boy!" The mourning mass burst apart, as if riven by a lightning strike, everybody falling back and anticipating a fight at the graveside. It was a trigger for four men, probably already designated as minders, to hustle the driver towards one of the cars and to drive off. Brian stayed at the graveside, aware that he had virtually no control; neither had the police. They all watched a group of people determine their own outcomes and make their own rules. This grievance was now a vein of bad blood which would stretch across decades and generations. Yet Brian was confident that somebody was in control and he suspected that it was the two fathers; that they had decreed that the funeral would not descend into a farce. The funeral quietly petered out as people drifted off. There was the odd heated conversation or shout of farewell, the nervy fumbling hands holding a calming cigarette and the slamming of car doors. Brian watched his staff laying the wreaths, one hundred and forty two of them, beside the soon to be backfilled grave. He cast an eye over the wreath cards and the most prominent word was, love!

His was a strange job, he thought, the proverbial fly on the wall. These communities, who despised the police, ignored officialdom and lived by their own rules, had to allow him to get in close, close enough to see their warts and all. They needed a funeral director and funerals were one of the few concessions, perhaps the only concession that they made to conventional society.

As he walked away from the graveside, Brian looked up at the massive, and guileless, wooden face of a Lakeland pony, its mane flowing down the contours of an aged, dead beech tree. It struck him that Ben was a jammy devil! He had employed a local artist to carve this dead stump, something he had done elsewhere in the cemetery. At the time, Ben had forgotten that the plot, on which the tree stood, was favoured by the travellers, the Gypsies of old, all horse fanciers to a man. This often maligned group were not used to being feted in any way, especially by council bureaucrats. They were ecstatic and convinced that this tribute to them was Ben's doing, and his alone. He was elevated, not enough to be socially embraced, but no longer to be seen as the enemy. Ben was surprised by this unexpected reverence, but made no effort to dispel the notion that it was intended.

Brian sped back to the yard and some hours later he was directing a funeral at a small cemetery on the outskirts of Carlisle. It went well until the lowering of the coffin; it descended about a foot and then jammed on the sides, refusing to drop the required six feet. With around one hundred people looking on, the urge to stand on the coffin and jump up and down was appealing, but had no aesthetic merit. So, Brian had to withdraw the family whilst the cemetery staff removed the grave shoring, and widened the grave. Within ten minutes, the problem was overcome but Brian knew that nearly all the people at the funeral worked for Carlisle Council. He sensed that Ben was annoyed at such an embarrassing cockup. Fortunately, the family did not appear too upset and Brian avoided giving any indication of whom or what, was to blame. He said that he would investigate it.

When Brian returned to his office, he immediately checked the details of the coffin size sent to the cemetery office and, as he had feared, they had given the wrong measurements. His dilemma was whether to admit responsibility, or to sit back and see what, if anything, happened. Also, if he admitted to the error, he would have to reduce the funeral account as a goodwill gesture, so he wrestled with the decision overnight. The next day, he decided that honesty was the best option, which proved to be a good decision. When he contacted the family, they already suspected that the fault was his. It transpired that the cemetery staff, all too aware that funeral directors often shifted the blame on to them, had made sure that the grapevine within the council had the right story. Brian, after initial relief that he had made the right decision, realised that his reputation, rather than being damaged, had been enhanced. He would be seen as an honest funeral director, even if a little incompetent. There was something satisfying about it.

His satisfaction was short lived. Like all funeral directors, he found it embarrassing when errors occurred and it was constantly on his mind. It was always worse when it was something really simple and obvious, like a coffin getting stuck. He was acutely aware that a funeral was a performance. The audience had a level of expectation, not least that the coffin should get to the bottom of the grave. It was like a wedding, you only got one chance to do it properly, and it had to be right.

Brian was lucky this time, the family, thank God, had a sense of humour and saw the funny side. They had no intention of putting in a complaint. Brian was always intensely irritated when people suggested that his job was easy, that the dead never complained. They always think it's a joke. What they didn't realise was that the job was all about the living, and their sensitivity. What was funny to one person was a massive indignity to another, and indignity had to be compensated for.

Brian had to get his mind off the cockup because a family arrived to arrange a burial with him. Warning bells had started ringing immediately, because they seemed confused over whether or not they owned a grave. Only the previous year he had had to cancel a burial at the last minute, and it was not something he wanted to repeat. That family had said that they owned a grave in which their late father was buried, and they thought that there was still space for at least two further burials, a fact that the cemetery office had confirmed. But they didn't possess the grave deeds, so Brian had arranged for them to sign a statutory declaration. In that, they stated that the deeds were lost, and that they were the heirs of the long deceased grave owner. The day before the funeral a man had walked into the cemetery office upset that his grave had been excavated; he stood in front of the staff as if to use his body as visual evidence that he was hale and hearty! He proved to be the legitimate heir and that the other members of the family were estranged. The funeral had to be cancelled and another grave purchased by the counterfeit heirs. Brian could not understand why people would think that purloining a grave was not actually theft. His confidence in people wavered at times like this. The old funeral directors had told him how things had changed, how perjury had been unknown in the fifties and sixties, but now you couldn't trust anybody.

With this family, Brian was wary. There was almost desperation to use one of a number of old family graves but numerous enquiries to the cemetery office had all indicated that there were no spaces left. Finally, they recalled a family burial about eighty years previously. Sure enough, space existed for a further burial and the family were clearly relieved not to have to buy a new grave. The grave owner was already interred and nobody had taken over ownership, but they did not have the grave deeds. Were they entitled to use the grave? So, to play safe, Brian got them to sign a statutory declaration in front of a commissioner for oaths, in which they stated that there were no other heirs alive and that they were legally entitled to be registered as the new owners.

Ben had introduced these declarations because so many people were falsely claiming entitlement to old graves. It ensured that neither the cemetery staff nor the funeral directors could be held responsible. Brian could not understand why so many of his associates had castigated Ben over this, arguing that it was bureaucratic and that they had managed fine without it since Victorian times. But he was not one of those. He recalled that a few years ago, a man had walked around the cemetery, selected an old grave, and using details from the memorial inscription, claimed that he was the heir of the grave owner. Years later, the lie was discovered when the real heir contacted the cemetery.

Brian had observed that some people were more than willing than others to cheat if it was to the council's detriment, such as avoiding the cost of a new grave. Some of the funeral directors were complicit in this because they encouraged claims even if the family links were suspect. It was all part of an age old conspiracy to knock the council, to flag them up as the problem. After all, they put up fees, increased bureaucracy and made onerous rules, all of which made it expensive to die. It suited the funeral directors to be seen as advocates for the bereaved and opposed to officialdom. Demeaning the council was clever displacement. It was as if the families were so focussed on the council as the villain of the piece that they hardly noticed when the funeral director presented them with a big bill. It occasionally amazed him that the family actually thanked him for the bill, as if he were performing some sort of social service.

The widow was probably in her early sixties, and she was still attractive. Brian had handled the cremation and, two days later, the burial of the ashes. Weeks later, both now stood, side by side, with Ben, staring at the grave. Brian knew she had been fretting about the grave location since the day of the burial. It was near the back of the plot, up against a high beech hedge. Not wanting to know, she had left the grave selection to the cemetery staff but had not realised how shaded it was at the back of the plot. She felt that it did not reflect her husband's character and she reminisced about how he used to be a band leader, always at the front and in the limelight. Brian knew that what might appear trivial to others, would continue to cause anxiety to this woman and ultimately, illness. Ben realised that to resolve the problem the only option was to elevate him from the position of percussionist to his rightful position as bandleader. They were agreed. An application to exhume the ashes was prepared, and the casket moved to a grave on the front row.

With the bandleader positioned to conduct for eternity, Brian turned his mind to a baby. Widows and the elderly were his speciality; battered babies were not! He had been shocked when he saw the body and was filled with revulsion when he thought about the perpetrators, the mother and her boyfriend. It had not been an easy funeral to arrange especially with all the police involvement. At the funeral, they detained the mother in the rear seat of a car, parked on the cemetery drive, but they would not let her go to the graveside. Brian could see her face, pressed against the glass, staring out, but he was too far away to see if there were tears. The baby's father and his brother carried the white coffin to the grave, whilst she looked on. The boyfriend was in custody and, not being a blood relative, the police would not allow him to attend. Photographers from the press were secreted behind trees as Brian lead the mourners to the graveside, mostly young and poor, their cars rusting heaps parked in a long line up the drive.

Brian knew that this was a modern take on the Victorian pauper funeral, and not many years ago the burial would have been in an unmarked communal grave. But here, in Carlisle Cemetery, it was in a new plot called, The Babies Memorial Garden. Old trees created a lovely setting and each baby had its own little grave. Here, nobody could tell whether you were rich or poor, at least, after the rusting cars had left. Looking around, Brian could calculate, using the presence or absence of teddies and toys, how often parents were visiting the various graves; painful expressions of their loss. He knew that one mother had buried three stillbirths here and a number of graves held foetal remains. He was pleased that he did baby funerals for free, they were something he would not want to profit from.

Later, Brian held his breath as he watched a coffin faultlessly lowered into a grave. The sister of the deceased, who stood beside him, broke his composure with a sudden outburst, "I want to take him home", she shouted. Brian wished she would make her mind up. Only minutes earlier she had shouted, "I want to take him into the kitchen." A member of the family, trying to humour her, in the hope that it would keep her quiet, a sentiment Brian was in sympathy with, responded by saying, "But he is with you always." Brian wondered how on earth the medics knew when someone had actually gone mad.

Brian was niggled, and too preoccupied with negative irritations. It was his accountants fault, after he had told him that his funeral numbers had dropped by fifty over the year. He had known that and it didn't help that his wife had reminded him that he needed to review his business strategy. There had been interminable discussions and the evident conclusion was that he was the problem. It was not just that he was too stuck in the old ways; it was that this was all too obvious to everybody else. His wife had identified his nemesis on too many occasions; it was Roger! It was all too upsetting and what was a nemesis anyway?

†

At dinner, Roger was spooning his desert and surprised his

wife by bursting into laughter. At first she thought it was to do with eating his favourite dish, stewed dried apricots, which he called, dead mans ears. It was a term he had stolen from the US. But no, he explained, it was because he was thinking about a funeral earlier that morning, at a rural churchyard. This was situated inside a Roman Fort, along Hadrian's Wall, and he and the bearers were talking to the sexton who dug the graves. He was explaining that he often dug up Roman artefacts and on a number of occasions had dug down and found the remains of a Roman wall. The stones were too big to remove so he was then forced to excavate down either side of the wall. One of the bearers, casually chatting away, called the sexton a sextant, which the others smiled at but said nothing. Quick as a light, Roger had said, "No, a sextant is a gravedigger who is unsure in which direction the grave is facing!" They all laughed but he didn't know whether they really got the joke, or not.

Roger retained the smile up to the point at which he met four daughters intent on arranging the funeral of their late father. He arrived at the house only to find that they had started without him; there was a full scale fight on the lounge carpet. The second round timed with his arrival, and the atmosphere was electric. He soon realised that this was not a home in which anybody, ever, spoke calmly and quietly. The explosion of violence, on this occasion, was ignited by the father's religion. This resided vaguely somewhere between the Church of England and Catholicism, and the daughters were evenly split. There was the Papist pair in the right hand corner, tightly clutching their rosaries, verses the C of E pair in the left hand corner, tightly clenching their fists. It was unprecedented; he had never seen this before, two people so fired up about the Church of England! The sparring was interminable as each convinced themselves that they were gaining points. Roger knew that neither side understood the word dogma, yet they possessed a potent belief system. Every single point they gained derived from something seen on television, or in films. They knew virtually nothing about religion in a conventional sense. Roger finally rang the bell by suggesting that the funeral service could be taken by a C of E vicar that he knew, who, with a nod to the Catholics, liked to be called Father. This appeared to solve the problem.

However, later that day, the Papist pair called at his office. They wanted him to telephone all the taxi firms in Carlisle to instruct them not to convey the C of E pair to the funeral at the crematorium. His immediate thought was to remind them that the buses were not on strike and that their sisters still had the use of their legs, but he decided on just a flat refusal. Afterwards, he thought it might be helpful to telephone the crem staff to let them know that there might be an example of religious intolerance at the two o'clock service on Friday; fisticuffs!

†

Graham had been invited to the consecration of the new burial plot in a rural parish churchyard. Unlike in the past, a consecration by the Bishop was a rare spectacle, so Graham was keen to attend. In recent decades it had become a paper exercise, just an administrative formality in an office with plans and signatures. For some reason, the Bishop had promised the local vicar he would preside on the day, and it was an opportunity for the church to gain some media attention, reminiscent of when it was a real power in the shires. Graham had never been to such an event but he knew enough about consecration to understand what was going to happen.

There was a small marquee in which a cup of tea and cake was provided, and a respectable number of parish councillors, villagers and churchgoers were in attendance dressed in their glad rags. The mortal Bishop looked resplendent and, after reciting a few prayers, he headed a small party in procession to the four corners of the new burial area, and, striking the ground with his mystical staff, ceded the plot to the jurisdiction of the Church of England. It was now God's acre, but only to those of the established church, the Church of England. The law, however, not keen on this exclusivity, dictated that the graves could be used by the dead parishioners whatever their religion or lack of it, provided they were prepared to lie within the embrace of the Church of England. It was still the classic British fudge because the vicar retained the power to choose the grave position. All too often, the Catholics and atheists found themselves interred, side by side, and united only by the fact they were in the least desirable parts of God's acre, the unkempt, wet or mucky bits.

Graham was one of the few present who understood that the other religions considered this consecration ceremony unnecessary; they were confident that all the earth was God's. These believers and unbelievers could avoid the churchyard but only if they had a parish or council cemetery in their locality, where they would be allocated nondenominational plots, which were unconsecrated and for all and sundry. Graham knew that most people did not understand any of this and were convinced that everybody with a religion was buried on consecrated ground.

One thing was certain, that you could tie yourself in knots with these issues. The Socialist Carlisle Council had tried to make one rule for everyone. They didn't want Ben to reserve special grave plots for the Church of England if other religions, and even atheists, were not given equal rights, but that meant allocating a separate burial area for each religion or belief. When they realised that this immediately required at least ten different burial plots, and, with a precedent set, the requirement to offer plots to anybody who professed a new religion, they backed off, because of the massive cost involved. So, the equal rights policy was turned around and it was decided that everybody would be interred in a nondenominational plot. Surely, they conjectured, if loving your neighbour was a commandment, they could not possibly object to being buried next to them. It would be far more inclusive and better than creating separate little burial enclaves all over the cemetery. But, Graham knew that Ben had failed to hold the line. Both the Catholics and Muslims had lobby groups working behind the scenes. None of the councillors approached wanted to touch it, and so the classic fudge was required. It appeared that some faiths were to be considered more equal than others. Ben was instructed to quietly cede them separate plots. They could only rest in peace if their neighbour was one of their own.

After the ceremony, Graham was handed a cup of tea by one of the villagers. "Lovely ceremony wasn't it, and we now have enough graves to last us years," she said. Graham could see that she represented the establishment, her world was old England and even if they didn't go to church, they were still C of E. But he said nothing, this was the British way; not to think too deeply about it.

CHAPTER TWENTY SIX

Hot Gossip at the Crematorium

Reverend Gray led the cortege, reading from his prayer book as if God were deaf, and walking with a distinct military bearing. Roger followed with his top hat under his arm. The six bearers, the team of gnomes, were shouldering the coffin into the crematorium chapel followed by the weeping mourners. The organ was being played quietly, and the staccato high pitched squeak which accompanied it created a harshly conflicting note. Roger ignored the noise now that he knew what caused it. Months before he had carried out a funeral service with Reverend Gray, he heard the squeak and as they were using the crematorium bier, he complained to the crematorium staff that the wheels needed oiling. The wheels were checked but there was no squeak. The staff suspected that it was not a what, but a who; the squeak was Reverend Gray! They all knew he had been an army padre and that he carried a leg injury; it was a leg calliper and it needed oiling. When they told Roger, he laughed but no one was prepared to mention it to the padre. From that day onwards, his discordant calliper was anticipated as an organ accompaniment.

Roger was aware that funerals were like that, the art of the impromptu. Only weeks before he had arranged a cremation for a local rock star, who was a Catholic. Roger prided himself in supplying coffins with the symbolism favoured by

Catholics, and on this occasion, the family had chosen an artistic model appropriately called The Leonardo. This had exquisite side panels illustrating The Last Supper, beautifully crafted in plastic. Roger, as with most people over thirty years of age, had forgotten that the current education police had removed all references to what people used to call the classical. Consequently, the rocking mourners at the funeral, due either to ignorance or perhaps being high on some divine substance, had mistakenly thought that the side panels illustrated the rock group Showaddywaddy. They were so taken with it that they all cheered as the coffin passed by.

Reverend Gray settled into the service but, as is so often the case in these modern funerals, a mobile phone went off and punctuated the near silence with a tinny tune. Afterwards, as Roger led the funeral party out onto the flower terrace to view the wreaths, he saw James Burns, a Scottish funeral director from the Borders, looking in his direction. He suspected that James was intent on speaking to him, probably because of his status within BALU, and, sure enough, as soon as Roger's family was driven off, he walked up. He was another funeral director who was always twining on about Ben, so Roger anticipated what was coming.

James was really animated and immediately disgorged the bile of the Scot when offended by an Englishman. His gripe was that Ben's staff had rejected the small casket that he had left at the crematorium in which to place the cremated remains from one of his funerals. It wasn't big enough to take all the ashes so they had insisted that he bought one of their larger caskets. He was so annoyed that he telephoned Ben to remind him that the caskets he used were accepted without question at the crematoria on the Scottish side of the border. Ben was having none of it and Roger sensed that he stung James by suggesting that he had sufficient experience to know that the caskets were much too small; that it was morally wrong not to give all the ashes to the family.

Roger realised immediately that James was not on firm ground but who wanted to argue with a Scotsman about the real issue, which was money? Roger knew that James wasn't the only funeral director who tried to get away with using caskets that were too small. How could he tell him that it was not really the done thing to save a quid on the cost of a casket, which was recharged to the family anyway, and then force the crematorium staff to separately dispose of the remaining ashes? He didn't quite know how to put it to James, or where to start, so he just heard him out.

Roger rode back to the office in the hearse, Reverend Gray seated behind him. The Reverend chatted away about a recent clergy Chapter meeting, to which Ben had been invited. They liked the many changes, especially the natural burials and the new crematorium times. Roger had no choice but to listen as he was told that natural burial was really quite spiritual and the clergy all thought that it wouldn't be long before the Church of England would have consecrated sites of their own. He then went on about the crematorium service times being extended from thirty to forty minutes, how this was much more relaxing for the clergy and made the whole thing less like a conveyor belt. Roger listened but said little. It was always a challenge when ministers showed support for Ben so he had to take care. At times he even wondered whether the clergy were deliberately taunting him, that they might report his responses back to the next Chapter meeting. As they drove back into Carlisle he was glad the journey was over. It was pouring with rain again and it had been the wettest winter for years, as if Cumbria wasn't already the wettest part of the UK. He seemed to have a permanent flush these days, what with all the wind and biting rain. His face felt, as one of his staff often said, like a smacked arse!

Over lunch, Roger reflected on the impact Ben was having. Only the day before, a man had called to arrange a cremation with him and he was alarmed by the environmental coverage that Ben had been receiving. The man knew that cremation had been lambasted over the past few years, and that this natural burial idea was said to be better for the environment. Roger could see that the man was disconcerted; for him, a lifelong confidence in cremation was being challenged. He was looking to Roger for reassurance; was cremation acceptable simply because it was what people had done for years? Roger was aware that even if his knowledge was superficial, it didn't matter. He knew what would do the trick; words like abatement and filtration inspired confidence, that the enquirer could discount the pollution issue and relax. Even if they had other issues with cremation, he could fall back on the fact that the alternatives might still be worse for other reasons. If they cited natural burial, were they content to be buried in an unkempt field that might also become unkempt woodland? It wasn't right, thought Roger, that bereaved people should be made to feel uncomfortable with cremation. One consolation was that he knew from articles in professional journals and from BALU, that Ben was taking a lot of flak from diehard cremationists, even in his own profession. Some people had actually lost their cool and berated him over his promotion of natural burial, not because it was a bad idea but because it threatened cremation. After decades of cremation being promoted as the only way forward, cremationists were suddenly on the back foot.

Roger knew that he wasn't telling the whole truth when he said that cremation was now clean. New laws were forcing crematoria to fit modern and impressive cremators that reduced pollution, but they consumed far more gas. He knew that it was the amount of gas being used that had first alerted Ben to the problems with cremation, even though up to the nineteen eighties, he too had been a staunch cremationist.

Roger mused over this, but he couldn't get too fired up about it. What nobody realised was that he, and all the funeral directors, didn't give a toss about pollution and gas consumption. They just arranged funerals and disposed of bodies. Once the funeral service was over, that was it. Admittedly, a cremation had the advantages of being quicker so they could do more funerals in a day, and there was no mud. And even if the family preferred to arrange a burial, he could usually sell them a memorial, but not if it was in the natural burial area!

Now, the irritation was that Ben was expecting them to show responsibility for what happened after the cremation service, not least the smoke given off by coffins. His staff were now using computers to monitor each cremation and this electronic finger was pointing at the coffins which smoked. Roger knew from Ben that his were okay, so far, but those who weren't were furious at being exposed by new technology. Roger suspected that the smoky ones were just a pound or two cheaper to buy in, but he wasn't going to tell Ben that.

His thoughts were interrupted as a family arrived, intent upon arranging a cremation. He did the greeting and meeting and shed a few tears. They wanted the funeral on the following

Wednesday afternoon, but he knew that he was already fully booked that day. He didn't want to say that he couldn't do it and risk losing the funeral, so he fell back on his usual ruse, the one which all the funeral directors used. He suggested to them that he would telephone the crematorium to see what times were available on Wednesday. He disappeared into the back office but when he spoke to the crematorium staff, he ignored Wednesday and only enquired about the times that suited him on the Thursday. On returning to the family, he apologised on behalf of the crematorium because nothing was available on Wednesday but 2pm was available on the Thursday. It wasn't ideal, they said, but if the crematorium was fully booked then it would have to do. After they had left, Roger's wife reminded him that one of these days somebody would catch him out. If they had been in contact with the crematorium before meeting him, they would realise why the crematorium always seemed much busier than it really was. "Yes, they could do that", said Roger, "But they never do."

The following morning at breakfast, the News & Star was a delight. On the front page, there was a picture of Ben squirming under the headline, 'Crematorium Destroys Wreaths'. Roger knew through the grapevine what had happened but when he saw it in print there was an added pleasure to it. One of the crematorium staff had removed and thrown away the wreaths from a cremation that had taken place only three days previously even though there was an assurance that they would remain on display for five days. This affront to the deceased and the fact that the wreaths were worth three hundred pounds was the lead story. Roger wished he could have been a fly on the wall to witness Ben standing in front of the entire family, at their home, like a naughty boy.

No amount of apology would erase this insult, especially when the lame excuse was that the employee had just got his days mixed up, and no, he had not noticed how fresh the flowers in the wreaths were. Such a distressing error must, in the family's opinion, warrant the employee being sacked for gross carelessness. A written warning would not be enough. The family didn't want to hear from Ben that the error was out of character for the employee and that he was normally diligent. The fact that such an error had never happened before meant nothing to them. They demanded compensation. The very least the council could do was to pay for the small memorial they intended to place over the cremated remains for their loved one.

Roger imagined that, in their indignation, they would seek a worthy memorial and have an extensive inscription in mind; there would be no change from six hundred pounds. Right, they felt, was on their side, and if their demands were not met they would continue with their press campaign against the council, and call in a solicitor. Roger didn't exactly feel sorry for Ben but he knew how difficult it would be to get the council to agree to such a high amount of compensation. They all made errors but the instant the council cocked up, they were vilified in the newspapers. The funeral director cockups, and there were many, never got to the media; their relationship with the family was different. The private sector kept it under wraps, complainants were quietly bought off and the profession was rarely exposed to the public gaze. Days later Roger was told that the council had paid up, as they always did under media pressure.

Roger's breakfast was cut short. Two of his staff were off with the flu, an epidemic that was sweeping the country, so he was called to help collect some bodies from the hospital. When he arrived at the mortuary all the fridges were full and eighteen bodies were laid out on the floor. It was damned annoying! He didn't want the bodies but the mortuary staff had telephoned his office earlier threatening action if they didn't collect the bodies that had been with them the longest. But Roger, like all the other funeral directors, only had limited rack space and no body fridges. He already had coffins piled one on top of another. Because his hearse and limos were booked to capacity and he couldn't hire any for love nor money, he was already delaying funeral bookings by over a week. In itself, that was no real problem, just as long as he could leave the body at the mortuary. It was a bizarre situation, the hospital had too many bodies, the funeral directors couldn't manage any more funerals whilst the crematorium had plenty of spare times. It was like a game of pass the parcel, the hospital had all the parcels but nobody wanted to pick them up. He knew that if it was bad in Carlisle, it was far worse down South. Funerals were being delayed by a month in some areas and a question had even been asked in Parliament about the distress caused by the delays. The News & Star had asked him for a comment on the problem; what problem, he had said! As he put the phone down, it had struck him that they were hardly coping with a flu epidemic that had lasted one month. Heaven help us, he thought, if we have to deal with a pandemic!

Roger, praying that he did not go down with the flu, finished his day on a funeral of a young man at the crematorium, yet another drug death. The minister taking the service was, in Roger's eyes, a real star. Since the new catafalque had been installed in the chapel, at great expense, the ministers taking the service had decided that it warranted a new performance. They were presented this opportunity after the catafalque, upon which the coffin sat during the service, was moved out of a side recess and thrust into the spotlight. This act had been prompted by complaints that the old catafalque was so recessed that the coffin could only be seen by those in the front pews. For those at the back, the deceased did not appear to be at their own funeral. Now, the coffin was centre stage.

Rather than being met with applause, many of the ministers were initially scathing about the new set. It was the curtains, to be precise, the double curtains, that were a step too far. It was too theatrical and not befitting a funeral, but Roger was in no doubt that it would work. How the hell could they whinge when they all saw themselves as unfulfilled thespians? He was right and within weeks, many of them had rewritten the script. The coffin could no longer abruptly disappear behind a thick, musty, velvet curtain. The deceased had to be eased from view, gently phased into another existence. This transfiguration hinged on the push of a button. The first press was the committal, symbolised by drawing the wispy voile curtain to separate the mourners from the deceased. Soft under lighting gently framed the coffin and the organ quietly played; it was ethereal. Then, for the finale, the minister would walk to the end of the catafalque, press a tiny electronic control secreted in his pocket, throw up his arms and, miracle of miracles, the velvet curtain would slowly and silently envelop the coffin. Obscured, it had flown, metaphorically at least, from this world to the next. Roger loved it; his families loved it!

The service ended and Roger led the mourners out of the chapel listening to Robbie Williams singing, 'Angels'. He now found the song loathsome because it was requested at every drug death. The moment it started it spawned a crescendo of weeping; it was pop spirituality. For Roger, it was less angels and more dealers, death and misery.

Jim, the crematorium supervisor, brought out the wreaths that were left on the coffin so that the family could view them before leaving. Before getting into his car, Roger asked him how he was after recovering from the flu. "I'm fine", he said, "I had a good night on the town last night. My pal told two girls that I operated cremators and the one, a right cracker, said he can light my fire anytime!" They laughed together, but inconspicuously so that none of the mourners would witness unseemly humour.

✝

The professor was standing with Jim, who was operating the cremators, and had just charged the coffin from his funeral. "Another widow with a liking for the bottle," said Brian, "She should go through quickly." He knew that with alcoholics it was almost spontaneous combustion. "Seems she was a cantankerous old sod, her usual comment to her three children was, you'll be sorry when I'm gone, but the truth of the matter was that they were glad. She was always falling over and got quite nasty when she was tanked up." They watched for a few minutes and Jim pointed out that the computer had switched the gas jets off because they were not needed. The temperature dial rocketed from 800C to 1000C in a matter of minutes; the body was fuelling itself. Brian could hear the roar of the expanding combustion but when he looked through the spy hole there was only a deep red glow; no shape or form was visible because of the sheer volatility in the chamber. Jim suggested that there ought to be a discount for these bodies because they used no gas. Brian then quipped that this could be called an incendiary discount. He wondered how he might present this to his customers; were they a member of Alcoholics Anonymous?

It reminded him that these granny guzzlers never went to AA and few knew outside the close family. He recalled another little old lady with the same weakness, whose GP was concerned about her declining weight. The daughter promised to encourage her mother to eat more, but she did not discuss the real issue with the doctor. That her mother had an alternative surgery; other people called it an off-licence! Whisky was her medication. The game her mother played was to conceal her consumption. It could be as simple as hiding the tumbler in a drawer, but was often more subtle. The whisky would be poured into an empty spring water bottle or added to an innocent bottle of coke, and casually imbibed over the day. Then the empties had to be wrapped in newspaper to go in the bin, and she bought hooch at a variety of outlets so that her alcoholism wasn't obvious. Her justification fell back on it being her one little treat, in an otherwise empty life. But her benefit to Scottish distillers was a detriment to the food industry; too much of one and too little of the other. She constantly talked about how much she enjoyed food, of the recipes that she once cooked for the family, but in reality little food passed between her lips. She ate only sufficient to ensure that her right arm could lift a tumbler off the table.

The daughter, an expert cook, realised that she could match her mother's guile by integrating alcohol into her food, so she developed what she called, lush recipes, with tempting names like, steak n' stout, port porkies and rum roulade. No longer was food and drink in conflict. Her mother put on some weight whilst tottering unsteadily between mealtimes, and lived another ten years before her liver finally succumbed. This daughter was clever and had been able to absolve herself of maternal neglect. Too often, Brian had noted, the ailing and long time dying old buggers seeded the survivors with a smattering of guilt, of vexation; just enough to ensure that no one would rest in peace.

CHAPTER TWENTY SEVEN

Too Poor to Die

"I am trying to arrange my mother's funeral myself, and I wondered if you could give me a price for collecting her body?" Graham, at Roberts's, took the call from Mrs. Turner and was immediately wary. There was no hint in her voice of despair or crisis, which was usual with funeral enquiries. There was a calm confidence, even a hint of challenge in her voice. As if she was aware of this, she said, "I've bought a coffin from the council." It was a shot over the bows; it was her way of saying, don't even think of trying to sell me an expensive funeral package.

She wanted a one-off price from Roberts's to collect her mother's body from the mortuary, place her in the coffin, and deliver it to the crematorium for storage before the funeral service. Graham was now prepared for these sorts of enquiries and calmly asked her why she did not want a traditional funeral. He was always careful how he chose his words, staying away from the term, normal funeral, used by some funeral directors to imply that the request was abnormal. She replied that his traditional funeral would be over a thousand pounds and she didn't have that kind of money. Graham couldn't refute what she said and moved on to his next tack, whether the Social Fund would pay for her funeral. Was she or a member of her immediate family on benefits? No, she did not qualify for benefits and there was no financial help available anywhere else.

Graham was aware that his company now expected him to sow doubt, to test her resolve. He went straight in by asking whether she realised that she would not be able to view her mother's body if she did the funeral this way; that they didn't have any viewing facilities at the crematorium. Her reply was quick, as if she had rehearsed it before telephoning him. Her mother was eighty nine years old, which was ample time to have seen her and she was with her when she died. Graham could sense her irritation at his clumsy attempt to dissuade her and she sounded annoyed at his inference that she was arranging something second rate. He knew, at this stage, that it was prudent to back off and so he said he was sorry but Roberts's were not willing to participate in DIY funerals.

Graham recognised all the usual signs. The enquirer was always a woman; there was a certain grittiness, an expectation that their enquiry would be frustrated. Just like everybody else, she will have picked up the government booklet on how to arrange a funeral when she registered the death at the Registrars. She probably went to the Citizens Advice Bureau, but only a few, like her, persisted and ended up going to Ben's office. Graham could see that it wasn't just that Ben's staff knew the funeral business, it was more that they were not judgemental. They were the only ones who would impart confidence; yes, you can do that; yes, you can ask that; and yes, it's perfectly acceptable to ask about prices. Armed with that support, the Mrs. Turners of the world could face out the profession. Well, a few anyway.

It puzzled Graham. They must know that Roberts's would not get involved with such requests so why were they being contacted for a quote? He suspected that it was because Ben could not openly recommend a particular funeral director; it would show bias. His office actually gave people a list of all the funeral directors but he suspected that they must also have dropped hints as to who would be the most accommodating. What worried him most was that it wouldn't take more than a handful of successful quotes for it to be obvious how the funeral package was priced up.

He also felt sure that the enquirers had been told before they phoned that Roberts's was not, as they might have thought, a family firm but really a big company; that it was company policy not to sell anything but the full package. He was frustrated that he had just lost another funeral due to a policy worked up in head office in Manchester, but what could he do?

†

Roger took the call from Mrs. Turner, and he immediately recognised her as one of Ben's groupies because they all used certain words and phrases; they had been primed. Despite this, he had a sneaking regard for these women, unabashed in stating that they could not afford a traditional funeral. He had no qualms in quoting her a straight one hundred pounds, which she accepted. Afterwards, Roger sat back drinking a mug of tea. He felt somewhat smug because he had asked Mrs. Turner which firms she had approached; it was one in the eye for Roberts's. His policy was drummed into his staff. We never lose a job to another funeral director, no matter how much we give way. But it wasn't all win win, because Mrs. Turner would report back to Ben's staff. Although he knew that he would be considered an accommodating funeral director on Ben's list, it was still embarrassing, because he had been one of the members who had formulated BALU's policy to frustrate Ben.

Roger left the office to his wife and headed off to manage a burial. There was just the hearse and no limos, and they were meeting at the graveside. It was an unpurchased or common grave, no one would say the words pauper grave any more, but they would all be thinking it. The dead man in the back of the hearse was an uncommon funeral, even for a common grave. Roger knew many of the mourners from the man's circle. They had all driven themselves to the funeral because no limos had been ordered. They were all Mormons, but the deceased wasn't going to get the Mormon funeral they had promised him.

Today, they were mute observers, including the man Roger knew would usually have taken the service. They all stood around the grave, spruce in their dark suits and with a slight touch of arrogance imported from Salt Lake City. But today, they contrast with the Irish informality of the man's sister, aloof in her Catholicism and yet slightly bucolic. She was dressed as if the same clothes could be worn at a funeral service and for milking her one cow. She was patently isolated, because, until a few days previously, the deceased apparently had no family and no money, so, his church community had arranged a funeral befitting a Mormon. Then, from nowhere, in she swept, like a female St. Patrick, reminding the English and the Latter-day Saints, that, as he came into the world a Catholic then he will go out of the world a Catholic. Her spiritual conviction was strong, but her wallet weak. She could afford a basic funeral, and a priest, but she couldn't afford to buy a private grave on the Catholic plot. So, he would have to

215

go into a communal grave with, literally, God knows who, possibly even a bunch of damned atheists. The Catholic priest, aware of the dogmatic dispute but unable to refuse the woman's request, spoke words of significance only to himself and the bucolic woman of Wicklow; the others were just uncomfortable silent saints.

Roger struggled to appear easy with the woman knowing that she would go back to Ireland feeling very smug and pleased with herself. She would never return to Carlisle and nobody would ever place a memorial because he lay in a common grave. Dead or alive, thought Roger, it's no fun being poor.

†

"Government must recognise us as the champions for the bereaved." This was Carl's answer when Ronson telephoned him to ask what was happening about the Social Fund. He went on, "We must focus on the fact that we pull everything together and that without us there would be no dignified and caring funerals." Ronson was tired of all this strategic nonsense coming out of BALU head office in London, but he had to appear interested if only to dispel the myth that his branch were a load of simple rustics and insignificant. Carl viewed everything on a national scale radiating from London, there were no people, just actions. He patronisingly told him, "It's no big issue, our lobby group in Parliament is supporting us and they are having some impact on ministers." Lobbies, ministers, Parliament, it was all gobbledegook to Ronson, thankful that he was living on the edge of Empire. He asked whether anything was happening nationally with Ben and his

Charter for the Bereaved but Carl was immediately dismissive of Ben, wiping him out in one sentence; he was nothing but a shit shoveller out in the sticks and of no interest to BALU. He reminded Ronson that down South they had similar vocal irritants; Nicholas Albery at the Natural Death Centre, and Lord Young of Dartington, the founder of the Dead Citizens Charter. Ronson finished with, "Do I need to do anything here in Cumbria?" He immediately recognised the question as another rustic irrelevancy but it was too late. With just a hint that he considered everybody outside the metropolis a bumpkin, Carl said, "Ronson, don't you worry, you can leave this safely in our hands, we have a grip on the issues."

Ronson mused over his conversation with Carl as he set out for the BALU meeting. Everyone thinks we're a brotherhood, thought Ronson, but really we all have our own agenda. He had always felt less vulnerable in south Cumbria because he could ignore the changes in Carlisle, even if it was only thirty miles away. He had no choice but to take cremations to Carlisle, but he could ignore the natural burials. But what of Roger? He was Ben's fiercest critic, yet the BALU members were openly discussing an obvious fact; Roger's business was booming. They had no proof of how many funerals he was doing but in newspaper obits his firm's name was prominent and increasing year on year. He constantly attacked Ben as anti-funeral director but they all knew he worked with Ben when it suited him. On arrival at the meeting, he met Roger and warmly shook his hand; it was his turn to buy the drinks!

Ronson, Roger and the members were soon upbeat and laughing. HQ might think Ben was quiet but Roger, now the raconteur, related his latest shenanigans; Ben wanted to be a funeral director. Well, not quite, he wanted the council to front it, to advertise a basic funeral at a set cost. The members all knew it was the socialist buggers on the council, working through their anti-poverty forum, and convinced that funeral directors were ripping everybody off. The councillors seemed to think that they could do a decent funeral for far less than the professionals were charging.

Fortunately, BALU had them by the short and curlies! The council could not be a funeral director because of a handy little legal clause. To be a funeral director, it was necessary to transport bodies, and the council did not possess the powers to do this. The only option open to them was to specify, in writing, exactly what a basic funeral was, and then agree a fixed price contract with an existing funeral director. As if that was not difficult enough, the price itself had to be low and it was also their intention to advertise this in the press. It had Ben between a rock and a hard place. He knew the BALU members would close ranks so he played cute and quietly approached those funeral directors who were not BALU members. They all backed off, frightened of the repercussions; nobody was going to advertise a funeral price, and especially not a cheap one.

As they finished their beers, Ronson quipped, "We kept the lid on that bloody socialist council. Everywhere else they've got rid of anti-poverty forums, but not that bunch of reds and nerdy activists; none of them will stop until they get a funeral for nowt. And there's Ben, driving around in his people's car, a BMW convertible. I bet the bugger voted for Thatcher!"

Eight hundred and seventy five pounds, this was what the Benefits Agency seemed to think they could do a funeral for,

Ronson reminded them, at the start of the meeting. The price had been set in the early 1990's and it hadn't gone up a penny since. What Ronson didn't say was that the government had capped it to stop funeral directors exploiting the system. It was because the civil servants didn't know what a basic funeral actually cost and, to frustrate them, BALU wouldn't say. This constraint on Social Fund funerals was a problem, especially where grave costs were high. Some London BALU members couldn't do burials within the eight hundred and seventy five pounds and people were forced to choose cremation. At this point, Graham reminded them that his firm's outlet in London wouldn't use some cemeteries because their new graves were so expensive. If they were dealing with families who had relatives in those cemeteries then it often created a lot of distress.

People were complaining, so the government had set up a committee to look at it again. BALU suspected that with one funeral in fifteen being paid by the state, the overall cost was also a significant issue. The BALU representatives on the committee needed the right image, one that assured government that funerals were all about care and that money was just a necessary evil. BALU worked to a time honoured script, that it was the care and support demanded by the bereaved that forced them to devote over fifty hours of staff time to create a funeral.

Ronson's members had heard all this before but they wanted to know what the other side had said; what about Ben, he too had been called to give evidence? Ronson explained that his submission was confidential but from what he had been saying, it would probably be the same old thing, that people were living longer and that there are too many funeral directors, and not enough bodies. Also, that the hearse and limos spent most of their time sitting in the garage and it all kept British funeral prices inflated. On this inflammatory note, Ronson closed the meeting, explaining that sorting out the Social Fund funerals was going to prove difficult. "Well, beggars can't be choosers," said somebody in the room.

So the beggars will be the choosers, thought Ronson, as he listened to Ben being interviewed on Radio Cumbria. Both he and Roger had been invited to speak with Ben on the same programme, but had refused. Ben recounted that he had arranged funerals and fifty hours was a gross exaggeration. Ronson was fuming. An exaggeration; why not just call us bloody liars? Ben had advised that twenty hours was realistic for a basic funeral on the Social Fund and government had obviously accepted this. Ben had also suggested that government should cap the funeral directors charge at five hundred pounds and pay all the cemetery or crematorium charges, called the disbursements, whatever they were. This would allow people to choose the cemetery or crematorium they wanted, even in London, and stop funeral directors exploiting the system.

Everything appeared to go quiet but Ronson knew that the men in black were meeting in London. As long term protagonists, BALU and all the other funeral directing organisations wouldn't normally be seen in the same room, let alone talk together. For once, they were united, and an instruction went out; a funeral would not be arranged for five hundred pounds; the figure was just too low. The strategy was that funeral directors would levy a supplementary fee to people wanting a Social Fund funeral. It would cover the difference between the cap figure and what the funeral director considered was the true cost. This would show government that they meant business.

It proved a mess! Most of the independent funeral directors took no notice. Their funeral package was often less than five hundred pounds already so they didn't require a supplement. Ronson, Roger, and most of the BALU family firms agreed a token supplement but, in practice, this was embarrassing to ask for when people were on benefits. The excuse that the government wouldn't pay them enough seemed lame. Then Ronson found out that the big firms were charging a much higher supplement and demanding it up front, in cash. This was because they doubted that people on benefits, with a poor credit rating, would pay the supplement after the funeral had taken place. It occurred to Ronson that, 'O death where is thy sting,' was probably written for people on benefits!

†

There were too many funeral directors and not enough bodies. Graham pondered over this because his funeral numbers were falling, something he was discussing with Eric, his Regional Manager. It was the telephone quotes; he lost every single one. Both knew that Roger and the independents just had one funeral price, they didn't have all the different packages. Graham felt that their problem was calling the cheapest funeral, basic. Even this was too expensive.

"The word basic jars, it sounds as though it lacks quality," said Graham. "That's why we use it," said Eric, "We considered other terms like simple funeral and economy funeral, but they were not favoured." "Why?" said Graham.

Eric continued, "The Office of Fair Trading pushed the industry on this point, but our argument was that words like simple, and economy, had various interpretations in different parts of the country." "Did they accept that," said Graham. "Well yes, ultimately, but they weren't happy." "Why did you play with words in this way?" said Graham. "Well, we also felt that simple, and economy, spoke too much of costs, that the words suggested a funeral was just a matter of providing coffins and moving bodies around. It didn't highlight our support and care for the bereaved, that there were components they could not see. The word, basic, was our way of saying that those unseen support elements had been removed. That in order to reduce our charges we simply provided less care and support to the bereaved."

Graham thought he understood this but asked Eric if the Office of Fair Trading had accepted this argument. "Well, they had little option but were not happy. They issued a statement saying that they had investigated the funeral market on a couple of occasions and were concerned about market distortion and lack of transparency, but they could do nothing. Let's face it, there're pretty toothless."

Graham said, "So if we have to stay with the basic funeral, is there any chance we could break down the package and offer just individual components?" "No," said Eric, "You know that company policy is to sell the entire funeral package." "So I have to continue losing funerals?" "Yes," said Eric, "But it's a small number so don't worry. Low turnover with a high mark-up, a quality service, that's the way the company works. Everybody knows we are expensive, which is the whole point. It's a virtue rather than a weakness; its funeral status!"

CHAPTER TWENTY EIGHT

Rentacoffin

Graham couldn't walk into the natural burial plot without a snigger. It was Thelma's fault after she told him how Ben was originally going to buy a grave for himself, the first grave, right at the entrance. It was to be his equivalent of the personalised number plate, the prestigious WB1. After death, he would lead his green legion from the front, the sentinels a mass of grave oaks stretching out into infinity. Thelma took a more pragmatic view to make Ben see sense, "Imagine, that for the next one hundred years every funeral director leading a funeral into this plot will spit straight on your grave!"

Graham looked out over the burial site, an ever expanding woodland and knew that Ben now had an anonymous grave, hiding amongst the oaks. He also knew that Ben recounted this spitting story during his heritage walks around the cemetery. It was usually after he had told his audience that it was his wife who was responsible for him buying the grave. He had been surprised when she requested a natural burial grave for her Christmas present. But, when she was dropping hints about her present twelve months later, his response had been, "Surely you don't expect anything this Christmas; you haven't used the present I bought you last year!"

That's Ben, he thought, a man who even used his wife for promotion, virtuous not because of her fidelity, but because she was green and chose to buy a natural burial grave. He could visualise Ben's funeral on this plot and thought of the old funeral director's joke; that's Ben, the atheist – all dressed up and nowhere to go. It struck him that thoughts of Ben and his green funerals no longer appeared a threat. Personally, he felt no animosity because he found the green funerals interesting and all the Carlisle BALU members were now doing them routinely. It was needs must but only if the family initiated it. At the first mention of a natural burial, they all put on their environmental face and supported Greenpeace. They quickly realised that, unlike funeral directors in other parts of the country, they could create a funeral that was really meaningful to these people, and the families were very complimentary. The compliments had benefited Graham within his company and gave him a lot of kudos. What started as a threat now put him at the cutting edge. In his firm, he was the most experienced green funeral manager in the entire country.

The fact that his company recognised his green funeral skills wasn't always an advantage. One of the London branches had put a young man with terminal aids on to him. He had wanted natural burial but Graham had to explain that it was not available where he lived and it was obvious that the cost of his funeral coming to Carlisle was out of the question. The man was deeply upset. But Graham still glowed when he thought how impressive his CV looked; specialist in green funerals. The enquiry from London suggested that he was now expert in the British way of death. The next time he updated his CV he needed to make it clear he was not working in the sticks. He would quote Jonathon Porrit's article in the Daily Telegraph stating that 'Carlisle City Council is the pioneer of the new natural burial movement.' That would look good, he thought to himself.

Graham had noted a sea change in the past few years. Parochial little Carlisle had become the UK's green burial centre; it was becoming fashionable, de rigueur so to speak, to be buried under a tree. The local rag, The News & Star, had even written an item on Ben called, 'Profile of an Iconoclast', suggesting that the Roman city was a centre of environmental innovation, even if it was only on funerals. It was helped in no small measure by the God fearing Scots, whose councils continued to think the idea pagan. Consequently, Graham's company was now bringing bodies from as far as Edinburgh, over one hundred miles away, for green burial in Carlisle.

Even so, despite all the publicity, Graham could not assume that people understood green burial. Some thought that the graves were reserved for pagans, or for people doing DIY funerals. It was the media's fault because they always presented a slightly distorted view to fit their own anti-funeral director agenda. So, Graham became adept at defining his clients. The true greens were easy, especially if they turned up on a bicycle and were wearing an anorak. Others displayed their colours as bird-watchers, beekeepers and organic gardeners. With these people he would enthuse about the company's wicker coffin, and the promise of an oak tree was more than enough. They were the lifestyle greens. The difficult ones were those who wanted to appear green. They had the vision of the life giving oak tree but it sat on a mown lawn that was neat and tidy. To them, the word habitat was a retail store, not a patch of long grass that nurtured creepy crawlies. His danger then, was to appear an advocate, to encourage them only to find that at the first sign of long grass and mice, well, voles really, they would be back in complaining of neglect. They hadn't realised that it would be so wild; surely the grass could be cut a little more often? Graham had no intention of being blamed for their ignorance and they would never be able to say that he had recommended it. He knew it was strange, bizarre even, that he had no compunction about being an advocate for cremation.

As he walked into the natural burial plot he was aware of the unseen demarcations. The early burials were mostly offcomers, many radicals taking a stance against cremation. One, he recalled, was the winner of a national poetry prize and another, the author of a book on Durham Cathedral. But in the more recent graves there were far more Cumbrians and it was to one of these plots that he lead the cortege. The grave was set in a mass of rough grass; he could hear the crickets buzzing in the bright sunshine. As the cardboard coffin was placed on the putlogs over the grave, the crickets were silenced by Eddie Fisher singing, 'Oh My Papa'. When the CD ended, the Church of Scotland minister read prayers interspersed with family members reading secular poems and a eulogy. This papa loved walking and birds and, in their own way, the mourners redefined him. His physical remains would nurture the embryonic oak to be planted on the grave and his spirit released into the arms of nature. Graham found these funerals less sad, perhaps because the emphasis was on creating new life. Perhaps it really did lessen the sense of loss.

Graham had been surprised, shocked even, at just how varied these new funeral services were. They weren't constrained by the restrictive conventions of the crematorium. The contrast was refreshing, that within one hour he could move from a slick cremation to one of these natural burial funerals. It was rare for him to be touched emotionally at cremations or conventional burials, but here it was different. All of his senses seemed to be in play. Was it the spiritual proximity of nature?

Graham concentrated on the funeral, as a mourner drew a huge jeroboam of Islay malt whisky out of a protective box, and glasses were passed around to be filled; one remained on the tray, for the deceased! There was an air of expectancy. The minister spoke the committal and the tot for the deceased was poured over his cardboard coffin. The mourners then drank a toast to a Scot being buried in the green borderlands. The peaty aroma of good malt suffused the graveside, the coffin steaming in the warm sun.

†

Roger was standing outside the crematorium entrance, ready to join his gnomes on bearer duty. One of his managers was directing the funeral, so he could relax. He stood at the end of a row of five bearers and, at fifty five years, he reckoned he might be half the age of each of the five men. It was an exaggeration, he knew, but he smiled nonetheless. He employed these old buggers at just twelve pounds each per funeral. They used their own transport to get to the crem, but he provided a dark suit. It was cheap and easy but it had one flaw, their sudden disappearance. Sometimes into hospital or an old folks' home but occasionally, they just dropped dead! This was a double edged sword; he lost a bearer but he gained a funeral.

He knew Ben was concerned about this money saving ploy because he considered the men too old and that it was only a matter of time before one of the bearers collapsed, and the coffin would be dropped. He accepted that his bearers looked as if they had problems drawing their pension, let alone drawing a coffin out of the back of the hearse. The big effort was the lift from the hearse deck and up onto the shoulders. In the past, the coach-built hearse decks were much higher but in recent years practicality had been sacrificed to the sleek, low slung American style hearse. The coffin was now much lower; the contents much heavier. So rather than wait for the inevitable drop, Roger often positioned himself at the head end of the coffin to assist with the lift onto their shoulders. They hadn't actually dropped a coffin – yet!

It was different today because the family had chosen, 'The Carlisle Coffin'. In truth, it wasn't a coffin; it was a coffin cover. To those in the know, the real coffin was the cardboard shoebox secreted inside. The cover was made of real wood. It was poplar, much lighter than oak but polished to emphasise the beautiful grain. Running the full length, on each side, was a solid brass carrying rail. Not the usual plastic handles but the real deal, ones that could actually be used for their intended purpose – to lift and carry the coffin. The usual veneered, chipboard coffins, with their bogus handles, were a pig to lift. The gnomes had to fit their arthritic little fingers into notches cut on the underside, just inside the coffin edges, which was dammed awkward; especially when you were eighty five.

So, Roger thought, this is Ben's rentacoffin, another of his bright ideas but he had to admit it looked damn good and covered up the cardboard coffin. Ben hadn't been able to ignore the main criticism of cardboard; it looked cheap. People had to have the courage of their convictions to use one, and not many did. So he arranged for a specialist firm to create a classic Victorian, hand-built coffin, large enough to contain a basic cardboard coffin. The family bought the cardboard coffin, but hired the cover for the duration of the funeral. Then, after the crematorium service, the crem staff removed the top, raised the end panel and slid out the cardboard coffin for cremation.

When the rentacoffin was introduced, Roger and the BALU members did as they always did with Ben's ideas, they ignored it. The trouble was, the smaller independent funeral directors immediately took it up. Its advantage had nothing to do with being dirt cheap to hire or because it saved the world's resources and reduced pollution; it was because it enhanced their show, it had the wow factor! The independents all used second-hand hearses, usually old and ropy Ford Diplomats. But nobody noticed the state of the vehicle when this impressive wood and brass coffin was loaded in the back. People stood and gawped when it passed in the street; it was a coffin fit for celebrities; it must have cost thousands!

The media loved the idea and when they interviewed Ben he had his little digs ready. After describing its use and advantages, there would be a telling pause. Then, he would remind listeners or viewers that the funeral directors could just as easily have introduced the coffin themselves, but they didn't. They had no intention of losing the sale of a lucrative chipboard coffin and had already denigrated the idea by calling it the rentacoffin. Knowing that the promotion of the rentacoffin wouldn't be a strongpoint of the BALU members, the council took a brave step and publicised its availability in the local freebie, the Gazette. The advert made it clear to the bereaved – if you don't demand the Carlisle Coffin, you won't be told about it!

The hearse was due at 11a.m., so Roger stood outside the entrance, side by side with his bearers, their hands over their nether regions. The hearse was punctual, the driver, aware that the boss was acting as a bearer, nervous about arriving late. The driver raised the rear door and Roger and the other bearers shuffled into position, three on each side, facing each other. They knew their position precisely, matched in pairs, short at the head-end, and very short at the foot-end. When the minister was ready, they drew out the coffin and, using the rails, lifted smoothly, shuffled a turn and walked slowly into the chapel. With his nose pressed up against the polished wood, Roger inhaled nostalgia; it was the smell of the past. He could ignore the present, the cardboard secreted inside.

✝

Brian had been pretty wound up about Ben and his green coffins, but he wasn't called the professor for nothing! He had a strategy. If a client mentioned a green coffin they could supply one; not cardboard, of course. That would be met with a raised eyebrow and the irrefutable fact that they were of such poor quality that they would sag and leak; they were not fit for purpose. Brian's green coffin was not cardboard, wicker, bamboo or papier-mâché, all of which lacked that essential plastic liner. His green coffin was the basic chipboard model but externally stripped naked of its plastic adornment. There were no plastic handles, no plastic screw caps, the plastic nameplate was replaced by wood and he could ignore the unseen plastic liner. He could now say, in all honesty, that his green coffin significantly reduced cremation emissions.

His strategy worked even better than he expected. People

accepted it without question but this naked model had an unintended promotional benefit. It looked really dull, so dull that the other pseudo teak and mahogany coffins in the display room were usually more appealing, and he sold more. Being green did pay, after all!

†

Roger was pleased with himself. His accountant had just told him that he was seventy funerals up for the millennium year and he knew Flynn's and Roberts's were going the other way. His success was due to word of mouth, as the marketing people would say. In a small place like Carlisle, he had a reputation for being affable and flexible; everybody knew he wasn't anti anything. He should have been out celebrating but he and his wife were at home having their supper. He told her that she should have made it egg and chips because Ben was now having a go at their fish and chips. He was telling everyone that tooth fillings were now the problem because the amalgam was full of mercury. After it was cremated, it was picked up by rainfall and dropped into the North Sea. It then went into the food chain and ended up inside our fish. Roger said that when Ben had told him, he had joked about getting our teeth into Cod! It looked as if the council would have to fit expensive filters, or demand that funeral directors overcome the problem for them. His wife was puzzled, wondering what Roger could do about it, only to be told that he might have to remove the filled teeth from the corpse before cremation. Roger had never thought that false teeth could be an environmental blessing, but the baby-boomers had messed it up. They had kept their teeth but only at the expense of a mouthful of fillings, so the mercury from cremation was on the rise for the next thirty years. As he swallowed his last mouthful of fish, Roger pondered whether this was a job opportunity; which was most lucrative, to be a funeral director, or a dentist?

CHAPTER TWENTY NINE

Obit

The obits was a job Graham enjoyed, in part because it ceded a measure of responsibility to the funeral director. It was an area where they definitely won out over people who would not use a funeral director. Without his influence, his shadow, people found it desperately hard to get the local rag to accept an obituary. A number of sham obituaries had been sent in over the years, each devised as a sick joke, usually by young male friends of the potential victim. When the 'deceased' read their own obituary, few had seen the joke. Some felt spooked; it was the equivalent of the black spot, Dr. Death knocking at their door! As the newspapers were threatened with prosecution, they automatically refused all obituaries that were not submitted by a known funeral director. Although they usually relented if a death certificate was shown as well as personal identification, the bereaved found it distressing to be doubted by some spotty young stripling in the newspaper office.

Graham felt sure that most funeral directors treated this job too casually. He could understand why. Obituaries were just a media vanity, a simple and often boring notice of a death, full of clichés but empty of truth. No wife beaters or drunkards ever died; everybody was loved for eternity, or at least until next week. Graham was always patient with people and he tried to inject some colour. A few of the bereaved were also far removed from that image of the depressed mourner, and they could be very funny. In teasing out information, he often had stock phrases like, "Did she say anything before she died," and all too often they would reply, "Did she say anything? She never stopped talking for over fifty years!" The trouble was, they would never let him put lines like that in the actual copy.

It also surprised him how often the bereaved would unwittingly demean the dead person, especially the ones who had not been a wage earner, usually women. A typical comment was that their late mother was just a housewife. That really annoyed Graham and he suddenly found himself acting as an advocate for these women. Often, in response to his questions, far from being an anonymous housewife, a son or daughter would come to a realisation that their mother had been quite brilliant in many ways. She would suddenly shine out as the heart of the family, and often the mediator or peacekeeper, and many were recognised as skilled cooks or seamstresses. The obituary, thought Graham, could be an awakening. The irony was that these people had obviously never appreciated the deceased's true worth whilst they were alive.

It might be difficult to glean information from children, but it was even worse when it was a ninety year old widower. Graham would look at the lined and tense face, anticipate the poor memory, perhaps Alzheimer's, and realise that the man was completely unaware that he was not so quietly farting every few minutes. There were times, thought Graham, when death was itself the only realistic solution. He wanted to make a plea for death but it was so difficult to put into words. It reminded him of Don Quixote and the line 'Well, now: there's a remedy for everything, except death'.

These days, people thought that they knew the answer. It was simple, repudiate mortality and live by the myth of the miracle drug, the one that suggested death was for losers; ageing was for losers. All this was making life burdensome for many old people. They would often say to him, calmly and serenely, that they had experienced a wonderful life but, with their health and peer group gone, they were out of time and place, incompatible with the modern world. Graham found that they resented being patronised by politicians and medics convinced that old age was simply mind over matter, or just an issue of medical support or political will. What the establishment would not accept was that death could be a good thing, that it could be welcomed, that it held no fear. This is, thought Graham, the first society that has ever had to face the fact that people could live too long!

†

Ronson was sitting in the hearse on the way to a graveside service, with the local minister next to him gabbling away about his current read. It was a book by a local funeral director, a BALU member whom Ronson knew. Everyone had been amazed when he had put his memoirs as a village funeral director into print. The forward to the book had said that it was about his service to the community and dedication to the bereaved. What troubled the minister was that it described a one man show, or to be more precise, a one man charity! It wasn't just that the clergy and the crematorium were ignored, but the absence of any payment. It was as if a funeral account had never been submitted over the fifty years. So, the minister asked Ronson, was his Mercedes a gift from some unknown benefactor?

Ronson was expected to laugh and did so; it also suited him to pretend that he had not read the book. He suggested that the man wanted to write his own obituary, and as the minister ought to know, all obituaries are a vanity.

†

Brian took the call from Margaret, a local Registrar of Births, Deaths and Marriages. Cemetery staff had just informed her that Martin, one of his young funeral directors, had cancelled a burial booking at the cemetery. He had said that it was because the body was going for cryogenics. Why hadn't she known about it? What was going on? Brian hadn't the faintest idea so he said that he would find out and call her back.

The national news had been full of it recently. The cryogenic fanatics, naturally, were the Americans. They were freezing their bodies in liquid nitrogen, at least those with big wallets and egos to match. At some stage in the future, when the cause of their death could be sorted, or a new organ implanted, they were to be defrosted. It was a Frankenstein moment, but only for neat deaths. Those smashed up in a car or jumping off the multistorey car park were best advised to spend their money elsewhere.

The problem for Margaret was that the person could be brought back to life and so, could not be registered as dead. With people dying and then being reborn, it would really mess up their statistics. Brian could see how the registrars now appreciated the advantage of cremation, the body effectively destroyed, all neat and tidy for statistics. So, to overcome this, the registration service had devised a special cryogenics registration process, a registration limbo or what statisticians might refer to as a deferred death. It occurred to him that if cryogenic regeneration was used repeatedly, perhaps by revitalising the body with limb and organ transplants, the person's death might be deferred for hundreds of years, perhaps indefinitely. He thought about the complications of keeping track of immortal bodies. Then, there was the awful thought; there would be no need for a funeral director!

When Martin was challenged, it proved to be a practical joke. When he had cancelled the burial, he knew that it was a simple change to cremation, but thought that it would be funny to say the family had opted for cryogenics. It was Brian, not Martin, who had to do the grovelling apology to Margaret. She was incensed, not only at the time she had wasted ringing the national registration office, but at having to ring them back to say it was not true, that it was a joke. Brian sensed that their interest had made her feel important, that Carlisle was a trendsetter. British bodies going for cryogenics were very rare so to have a case in Carlisle was astounding. So, she too lost face and had to apologise. Brian belaboured Martin about his stupidity and the harm it had done the business; he was a hair's-breadth from dismissal for gross misconduct.

Brian mentioned cryogenics at the pub that night and recognised that it might have been a mistake – better to have said nothing. One pal reminded him that there would have to be a new kind of obit because the person wasn't exactly dead. Then all the others started on how the obit would read. Forever in our hearts was invalidated; it was more forever in the tank. Where was the body stored until it could be taken to

America – in the Iceland store, somebody said, just after the frozen chickens! Then there were questions about whether the defrost instructions were attached to the body and was there a danger that frozen dangly bits, especially small ones, might snap off rather too easily. Brian was adamant that this wasn't a problem for him. Then, somebody said that the brain was wiped clean by deep freezing, that the mind would be blank. No problem for you then Brian, somebody added, you can still come back as a funeral director!

✝

Roger peered through the cremator peephole into the red glow. The cremation had been running for just under ten minutes and the remnants of the chipboard coffin burnt away as he watched. The body cremating was evidently a man; unless a woman had a penis! There it was, proud and erect, feathered in bright orange flames, a totem of a now moribund sex drive. This glorious erection always happened when a man was cremated, the loins heated for the final time; not by pheromones but by North Sea gas. Watching, Roger reflected on his own sexuality; was this all a man's life was about, this burning appendage? It brought to mind John Betjeman, something of a funeral star these days, now that poetry was more valued than prayers. This visionary intellectual, when asked what he regretted most as death approached, could say no more than many ordinary men laying on their deathbed; that he hadn't had enough sex!

If John Betjeman rued his past, then there was little hope for the rest of us, thought Roger, and what did women regret? He avoided any clichés about women's needs and returned to the potential regret in his own obituary. Ideally, his would say that he had been retired for many years; that he had got out of funeral directing before becoming one of his own customers. There was only one solution, to sell his business to one of the big companies.

It was an epiphany driven by his children. His was the classic independent funeral director story. To start poor, build the business, make money and move to a nice detached house in an affluent area. The kids found themselves at a good school, but it came at a price. They soon realised that when your father buries stiffs, it was like manna from heaven for the school bullies. They didn't talk of shame but neither did they ever paint him with his top hat or hearse in the art class. Now they were older and the family funeral business was not on their career agenda; they were not going to be untouchables.

As Roger left the crematorium and headed down the drive, he could smell the burning bodies! Looking east, towards Penrith, a pall of fetid black smoke hung against the Lake District mountains. It was a death peculiar to farmers; foot-and-mouth disease. To see the piles of animal bodies on Border Television was enough; you wouldn't want smellyvision. The odour from burning flesh that hung over the county was repulsive and every so often, with a wind change, it wafted toward a new and sensitive nose. It was clinging, pervading, malodorous death! It was bad for everyone, but it hit the farmers hardest. Suicide rates had increased but that word would be omitted from their obituary.

†

"What's it all about, Graham?" The widow had posed this

question as she reflected on her husband's early death, sudden and traumatic. It had laid waste her plans; the past had shrunk and in its new smallness, very little seemed to have been achieved; the tomorrow, which had always promised so much, had evaporated. She was alone, the future a stark landscape and, at that moment, very uninviting. Graham expressed sympathy, aware that it was a pat reply. He tried to infuse some sincerity but it never felt right. He was glad that few people posed such questions.

When he had started in the work with Bill he had been entirely dumb, fearful of getting into a conversation with the bereaved about death. Bill had always told him that the professional funeral director kept it impersonal, it's not your death, it's theirs! More recently and hundreds of funerals later, that fear had receded and he was grateful, but he still kept his opinions to himself. The way people dealt with death was a minefield but no matter how many reports he read about the impact of bereavement, he was amazed at how well some people dealt with it. He now realised that religion wasn't the answer, but neither was atheism. Perhaps, the people who coped best were the pragmatists, because they neither forgot the person, nor put them on a pedestal. It was as if they integrated the dead person into their ongoing life, carried them along as a talisman, the memories a source of strength. He never heard them talk of regrets. He thought that they were often the widows and widowers who had remarried late in life. What was obvious to him was how these new twosomes talked about their previous partners, as if they were all part of a quartet; two living and two dead. These people were so easy with their deaths, at least on the surface, and he found he could relax with them. It was the opposite with those who created a shrine around the dead person. The widow's weeds had been replaced by a different form of conspicuous mourning. They were going to be depressed, no matter what. Life had stopped, joy had ended. He trod on eggshells when he dealt with them.

He drove home beside the now unseen Hadrian's Wall, heading west towards the Solway Firth. A skein of geese flew across and towards the pink tinged Lake District mountains. He stopped, switched off the engine and waited as a herd of cattle meandered across the road to a milking parlour. The air was crisp and clean, there was almost total silence, just the occasional and distant bleating sheep. The crisscrossing vapour trails strewn across the sky implied raucous jet engines, but they were too far up to intrude. He loved this remote corner of Britain and enjoyed it all the more simply because he knew that he was just passing through; he was in transition. Driving again, he noted the pheasant bodies littering the verges. These birds, needing grit for their gizzard, were fatally attracted to the road and oblivious to crushing tyres. They reminded him of humans; blind and dumb combatants with death.

The next day, at work, Graham telephoned Ronson with the news; he took it as if it was a reprieve from cancer. He wouldn't be dancing in the streets but he might send a card – 'Good Luck in your New Job'. He would definitely avoid the one that said – 'Sorry to Hear you are Leaving'. Twenty minutes later, in the hearse, one of Graham's bearers, an ex-policeman, a man who had never lost the knack of keeping an ear to the ground, said, "Have you heard Ben is moving on, he's got a new job in Cardiff." Another bearer, expert in the curt obituary, said, "Ah! He's Gone West!"

CHAPTER THIRTY

Death Unstung

"Have you heard, it's Ben West, he's back from the dead!" It was a cryptic comment related to the fact that Ben had finally retired to Christchurch on the south coast. It was a town with a reputation in the funeral industry, the one with the highest number of pensioners in 2012 and so a nirvana for funeral income. But the spurt of Ben's name into the room had then to be explained as only the older BALU members had heard of him. A colourful narrative of his history was then recounted, some true and some tittle-tattle, and although Graham only half heard, he noted the use of many expletives. The upshot was that the North East Branch of BALU had requisitioned a cohort of volunteers to attend the opening of the Durham Woodland Burial Park, listen to Ben's address and to report back to the next meeting.

So it was that a stalwart group of male and female warriors, Graham included, attended the community hall dressed in a symphony of black and white. Graham was unaware that the cohort looked intimidating until he was collecting a cup of tea and a nearby woman, who was looking back at the warriors, said to an associate, "Who are they? They look like a bunch of nightclub bouncers."

It was classic Ben as he opened his address with humour, how he, as a cemetery and crematorium manager married to a midwife, was originally one half of hatch and dispatch, but after he introduced natural burial, a local doctor described the pair as sperm and worm. That he appeared before them today both as the worm and as an advocate of global worming. Graham was one of the few who did not laugh. He noted that some of his BALU colleagues were smiling but he forgave them their youth and the fact that they had never heard Ben speak before.

Graham could feel the itch emanating from the chip on his shoulder. Ben, after all these years and with a rapidly balding head, still saw them as the funeral mafia. It was the same genial delivery leading to what Ben imagined was profound observation, but the sentiment was unchanged: the men in black were Victorian, abhorred change and still hid the coffin chipboard under the veneer. Ben had always used academic research to back up his views. It was a sneaky form of displacement because it enabled him to step out of the arena for a short while and place an independent expert in his shoes. This time he recounted some recent research into how funeral directors perceived natural burial. Sure enough, thought Graham, the study reinforced Ben's prejudices in suggesting that funeral directors still found the new funerals uncomfortable, the informality clashing with the black suit, their mark of rank. Unable to embrace casual clothing, they had devised a compromise for natural burial – a change of tie! Some in the audience found this funny.

The cohort sat in silence but Graham imagined that within minutes of Ben starting to speak, they despised him. He was so sure of himself, the man who had been involved with over 100,000 funerals before he retired and then published a book on natural burial. With the exception of the BALU members, there was probably nobody in the room who doubted what Ben said. The talk lasted no more than ten minutes and Graham saw no reason to respond to questions. Unfortunately, one of his colleagues thought otherwise. He bravely stood up, puffed up his chest, and told Ben that he resented him coming up North to tell everybody that funeral directors were a rip off. The room fell back into stunned silence.

Graham knew that it was a mistake. The way to handle Ben was to ignore him. Ben responded by reminding the man that he had never used those words, that the funeral directors were their own worst enemy, deviously trading under old family names. He reminded everyone that in the North East, they had some of the most expensive funeral directors in the UK. Annoyed at hearing this, another of the cohort half rose and shouted out "My firm is not expensive" and then, lost for words, slumped back into his seat.

The antics of BALU members back in Cumbria flooded back, the way that Ben had riled them. Here it was again, the almost childish response, the tantrums. But Graham lapsed back into nostalgia, suddenly aware that nobody had replaced Ben, the silver surfing anarchist; that he was still a voice in the wilderness. Where are they, all those young activists, the new greens, who were going to step into his shoes and give funeral directing a hard time? Yet he had a grudging respect for Ben and his futile raging at the commercialism of funerals.

After Ben had finished, Graham was suddenly reminded that the opening of the Durham Woodland Burial Park was in conjunction with a book launch, another book about natural burial by two academics from Durham University. At the end of the meeting, Graham went over to where it was being sold.

He picked up a copy and glanced through the pages. He looked about and, aware that his colleagues were leaving and over at the far side of the room, quickly bought a copy.

Graham had never read a book about death and funerals before for the simple reason that there were so few. Ben's book on natural burial and this subsequent book were the only recent ones. It had always amazed him that nobody had written a book on cremation, the way most funerals went. Perhaps it was pointless anyway because he knew that he would never have read it because he was so familiar with the subject. Likewise, he had ignored the mass of memoirs written by funeral directors because they all had the same theme – how to become dead rich. Those authors were often the spoiled sons living on the legacy of their undertaking fathers.

Graham read the book with interest and reread parts, aware that it was really a bit too academic but he got the gist of it. The reason why he read the book was complex. He had been there at the birth of natural burial and knew it well, but where was it going next? He had recently been amazed when, without any warning, the Co-op had bought two natural burial sites, and then a third. They must think it has a future. The crack suggested that the big bosses saw it as a premium product because people would pay a high price for natural burial. Graham also felt the bosses were nervous and sought skills in this new kind of funeral, that they should not miss an opportunity. It amused him to recall how some years earlier the idea was considered weird. Now, even weird appeared to be profitable.

It also amused him to think that the book was slightly toxic; he did not want to appear a swot. He knew that it was better to absorb the information, lay it down and then dredge it up in dribs and drabs. It could and would emerge as comments from the grapevine or from the bereaved or a mixture of both. He experienced a few green funerals so nobody would doubt his sources.

The content surprised him because it was so much more than a book; it was an affirmation, one that boosted his confidence. As he read he realised just how much he knew about the subject, the mishmash of stuff crammed into the back of his head, filed in ranks of funerals. Page by page it gave the mishmash order, sequenced it and convinced him that he could write such a book as if the findings were his own. In fact, he thought himself more credible than the authors because he had actually experienced what they only found out through research. He already knew that the church was steadily losing ground and he had witnessed the massive increase in secular funeral services. Most of all, he too knew that people were seeking a more spiritual kind of funeral. As he read, his brain flicked up the families he had worked with and he could still recall the challenge of those occasions, that feeling of powerlessness, about how to turn a rushed thirty minutes at a bland crematorium chapel into something spiritual, something that had meaning for the families.

Ben, too, knew this and had pointed out in his talk the astounding ambiguity of cremation; that the technology of a cremator is identical to that of a waste incinerator. He'd described the situation in Croydon where 86% of residents were choosing cremation and yet almost 100% were violently opposed to plans for a waste incinerator. It was the blindingly obvious; that if cremation was just a waste process then it could never be spiritual. Why had this never registered before? But knowledge had to be handled carefully; his company managed a lot of crematoria and this enlightenment was not something they would welcome. Even so, it forced Graham to contrast forlorn cremation with the spirituality of a green burial. He had done many in his previous job in Carlisle and one only a week before on the nearby Pennine moors. He did not need research, he had been there.

Graham was ambitious but he found himself between a rock and a hard place; what to do? The funeral business had never been more complex and he knew much more than the academics ever could. That even in his company there were employees identical to him and yet they all dealt with the bereaved in different ways. It was strategic focus, about how the company handled people depending on the facilities available. Where the company owned or managed a crematorium everything focussed on cremation being the way forward. Even if it was unspoken, staff knew that it was employment suicide to even think of the process as polluting. They knew that, to the company, the cremation itself was incidental, the cremation income relatively insignificant; what really mattered was the ashes. The staff knew their role; to get the family to place them in their crematorium Garden of Remembrance. That was the real treasury to the company, a mass of lucrative memorial roses and engraved granite plaques.

Graham knew what the senior managers really noted. It was when a family chose the company crematorium even when a council crem was much closer to the deceased's home. That was a coup for the staff that made the arrangement. But all this completely changed in those areas where the company managed a natural burial site. Then, the staff were expected to become environmentalists, to wax lyrical about trees and vista's and how gorgeous it looked when the bluebells flowered. But it was benign environmentalism, greenwashing, as the Americans would say, and there was to be no defamation of cremation, the environmental enemy, as it were. In fact, the promotional emphasis was about how ideal the natural burial site was for placing cremated remains. That was the complexity; cremation and natural burial were ideal bedfellows simply because selling a memorial over the ashes was the goal. It totally conflicted with what happened at independent natural burial sites, those who told the truth and talked of cremation as the great polluter. Some of those sites actually refused to accept cremated remains in view of the environmental damage that the cremation had caused.

If that was challenging, here he was, in an area where the company owned neither crematoria nor natural burial sites, and so were forced to use council facilities, at least until the company could take them over. So cremation was back in favour simply because it was quicker and the company could complete more funerals each day; but the ashes still mattered. The staff had failed if they were left at the council crematorium, where they were soft on memorial sales. He needed to encourage the bereaved to transfer them to a local cemetery or churchyard and then the company's memorial division could start the hard sell. Somebody always noticed the moment the percentage of memorials per funeral dropped off, and that did the staff no favours.

Graham knew it was a big game, rather like a maze. It was full of distressed players, none of whom knew the way out. The virtuous company had to take them by the hand and show them the way out, to find them solace. Okay, this blissful state did appear as a high priced memorial made of cheap Chinese granite but who was to say that there was any ethical issue. Even the psychologists considered memorials therapeutic after bereavement. Graham had to play his part, to develop an intimate relationship and offer guidance in a particular direction. A comment slipped in here or there was all that was needed; the one about not scattering the ashes to the wind lead the charge. It was that inference that an unmarked burial or lack of a memorial correlated with abandonment, with forgetting the dead. It worked because so often, after placing a memorial, he was profusely thanked. It was as if he was expert in psychology, in recovery from bereavement. It didn't matter, or they disregarded, the fact that they had paid dearly to reach that condition. Graham knew the score. Success was his commission but this did not deny him his own philosophy. Crappy Chinese memorials and tatty plastic flowers were old hat; spirituality was the new future. The game might be his bread and butter, for now, but that did not stop him looking to the future.

Graham realised that Ben had got it wrong all those years ago. Sure, there were a few people wanting to save the planet but the majority were seeking something else, here and now; something that enabled the soul to go on. The secular British had simply lost patience with the resurrection; the absurdity of it all.

Graham mulled over this thought for weeks. It appeared intellectual but it was really much more prosaic. He needed the patter to be right when he dealt with these new game players, the ones who wouldn't enter the old maze. They sought purpose and continuity, and he could say the right things simply because he was a convert. The book was right, the body was a gift, a present to the natural burial site in much the same way as if it had been donated to medical research. As if that were not spiritual enough, he could take it up another level by pointing out that decay, that foul decomposition denied by American embalming chemicals, was ecologically sound, that the body fed the soil and created fertility. Forget mortality and think vitality, the making of new forms of life. He recognised his past doubt at all those religious services he had witnessed, those committal prayers for the deceased in which the corpse was stone dead, nothing but ashes and waste. For years he had seen the disbelief in the faces of the mourners when the vicar talked about resurrection. There was the lie of that bible punching Christian ranter, standing at the graveside, who used to say "And one day, dear friends, all the dead shall rise up out of this ground…"

A profound serenity mantled Graham. For the first time in his funeral directing life he was ready, ready for those conspiracy types who were convinced he knew something deep and meaningful about the purpose of life. He did, and he was comfortable talking about atoms turning into a tree, about the wonder of decomposition and its contribution to new life. It was a fact reinforced only that week on television by Dr. Brian Cox. The meaning of life was about whether the dead die at all!

He put that thought to one side. Company policy was predicated on the fact that the body was just a lump of waste, a thing to be disposed of simply because it had no further purpose. This analogy with waste flagged up the funeral as the last goodbye, the final memory so spend, spend, spend; nothing remains but the final show. He now knew this to be untrue: the funeral was not the end but the new beginning. He kept this to himself. In due course the company would identify the new way and change their philosophy; less a philosophy, more a new business model.

Graham walked in front of the hearse, cane in hand, up

the main cemetery drive. It amused him that he was wearing his top hat, yet his appearance was in complete conflict with his anarchic train of thought. This hat he wore to signify outdated tradition; it perched on his head to represent his role as a body disposer. The hat looked absurd at a natural burial site and he avoided wearing it. But with natural burial he now had a metaphorical hat, one he whipped on the moment somebody doubted cremation or seemed querulous about the conventional ways. As he donned this hat, his new vocabulary switched away from waste and loss. If not full of optimism, he was at least ready to accept that death was not in vain and that it had purpose. If they were Christian, he could paint the site as an earthly Garden of Eden; if they were secular, science proved they could be a tree. Whatever, it was imbued with spirituality. He could, if pushed to the furthest point, even accept the premise that the purpose of life was to stop breathing and for people to become as useful dead as they were alive. For some, more useful; as organic material, a gift to nature.

Graham tugged the putlogs from under the coffin and his bearers lowered away. He stood next to the vicar, a tray of dry soil in his hands, ready to sprinkle over the coffin as the committal prayer began: The vicar spoke:

"O death, where is thy sting? O grave, where is thy victory?"

THE END

p.s. Some advice; don't end up like John Betjeman – get lots of sex!

Postscript

What do you mean, you're depressed! What did you expect after reading a book on death? Those of you who have survived to the end, hopefully more about mortality and less about boredom, of course, might like to know what happened around this story. The good news is that global warming has been reversed, in part, a very small part, by natural burial. The early sites, such as Carlisle and Hinton Park (Dorset), are now established woodland with meadow brown butterflies and crickets within their burial glades. There is no need at these sites to mow acre after acre or make safe decrepit memorials; the funerals are proving meaningful and spiritual; the author will die a happy but a no less poorer man.

Those councils and private individuals who followed the Carlisle lead and opened a natural burial site often experienced funeral director resistance, not least the ones that prohibited chipboard coffins and embalming. Some of the private site owners overcame this by collecting bodies themselves, and bypassing conventional funeral directors. Natural burial expanded to embrace farm burial, orchard burial and wildflower burial, with allotment and vineyard burial more recently proposed. Golf course burial might be anticipated, the twentieth hole, the one that follows the bar. Natural burial, as a low cost option, which was the original idea, is still offered by farm based and charity operated sites, because they continue to restrict grounds maintenance expenditure. But it is often much more expensive at private sites, especially if they offer extensive infrastructure such as chapels. Too often, private sites want to sell more graves and have reintroduced mowing to improve the appearance of grave plots. Where they want to sweeten funeral directors, they also allow embalming and chipboard coffins. These are often attractive sites but they are not ecologically sound.

The bad news (yes, I know you expected it) is that mainstream funeral directing has become worse, with many adverse exposé on television (2013). Research has shown that whereas funeral directors are quite comfortable talking to you about cremation, they just ignore natural burial. Unless you raise the topic, they will say nothing. Likewise, neither will embalming be mentioned but it is routinely included in the package price under the heading of hygienic treatment. Green coffin choice has expanded dramatically from cardboard to wicker, sea grass and even wool, but the veneered, particle board coffin, pretending to be wood, remains a staple. When it comes to competitive pricing, the odd thing is that the funeral directors who do the most funerals are often the most expensive. They use 'outlets' and constantly shift the body backwards and forwards from central storage 'hubs', and yet the savings do not reach the bereaved. The independents, those who scorned BALU in the novel, are often the cheapest, but there are fewer of them. A small number of exemplary 'green' funeral directors are now trading.

The secular service is now commonplace although itself more complex. Initially a prerogative of the British Humanist Association trained officiant, other celebrants now offer nonreligious services, often through funeral directors, for a fee. If they are not Humanists, one might assume them to qualify as atheists or agnostics. Or are they Church of England? Perhaps their belief doesn't matter, but have they been trained? Companies like Civil Ceremonies Ltd. are making a good reputation for themselves in this regard.

The response of crematoria to environmental issues remains poor, with a few exceptions. Although new crematoria are required to fit emission abatement (filtration) to cremators, existing crematoria are programmed to add abatement over the next few years. The sophisticated equipment is expensive but all it does is transfer the filtered material into a large drum and this has to be stored, forever, as hazardous waste. Filtration doubles fuel use and this is where you can spot the concerned crematorium – do they cremate efficiently? Fuel use can be dramatically reduced if a single cremator is operated over long periods, which requires staffing shifts, and efficient management. For instance, seven cremations can be completed in a twelve hour shift using one cremator, which then becomes heat soaked and highly efficient. To have sufficient cremations to do this, they may need to store bodies overnight and not cremate on the same day as the funeral service. Too many ignore this and prefer to waste gas by pre-heating several cremators each day, doing a couple of cremations in each, and then shut down until the next day. Neither is fitting abatement to cremators environmentally sound if the crematorium does few cremations, say two or three each day, as is the case with many private crematoria springing up in the countryside. They should store coffins for up to three days, and batch cremations on one or two cremating days each week. Few crematoria, not least private sites, are transparent on such issues. Unlike in Germany and Scandinavia, no UK crematoria cremate continually over twenty-four hours, which is the most efficient process. A very small number of crematoria utilise waste heat from the cremation process to heat chapels, offices, etc. There are two more telling examples of a caring crematorium. Those that recycle wreaths are exemplary, and rare. And only half of crematoria, usually council operated, recycle the waste metal from cremations, such as hip joints and similar prosthetics. The income from this recycling, where it is under the auspices of the Institute of Cemetery & Crematorium Management (ICCM), is given to charity (£260,000 in 2012). If these matters concern you, demand information from your funeral director (if you are using one!) *before* you select a crematorium. Bear in mind that many funeral directors *and* crematoria are owned or managed by the same company.

Sadly, the situation in councils has become much worse. As at Shrewsbury (2011), many established crematoria, built by public money, are contracted out to funeral directing companies. And most new crematoria are built by the private sector, which creates local monopolies because the firm now managing the crematorium is often the one who owns the local funeral directors. As the novel shows, their staff are muzzled by company policy and Ben West would certainly not get a job with them. They have no interest whatsoever in offering you new ways, or cheaper ways, of doing funerals and prefer to maintain the status quo. With virtually no transparency, and clear evidence of restrictive practices, government and councils still see the private sector as virtuous. The councils who sell out have sacrificed the social and environmental good, because they no longer employ staff who are expected to challenge, or rattle cages, on behalf of the bereaved. Consequently, there are rarely any impartial sources of advice, and most anti-poverty forums have been disbanded. The view that councils have become moribund is born out by research in 2010 at Sheffield University. This proved that farmers, with virtually no bereavement experience, provided far more sympathetic and successful natural burial sites than many councils.

Funeral costs have dramatically increased. In part, this is because councils have increased their burial and cremation fees well above inflation, often whilst cutting services and sometimes cutting out skilled managers, like Ben West. Neither will you have noticed any funeral directors advertising prices recently. They say, of course, that to do so would upset you. But if the funeral directors will not advertise funeral prices, the council could and should arrange a fixed price funeral with a local funeral director, and advertise it, as they do very successfully at Cardiff City Council. An immediate way to cut funeral costs is to offer a direct cremation service whereby the bereaved telephone the crematorium and they collect the body in a van, using an inexpensive green coffin. The body is then cremated and the ashes returned, in a casket, say in forty eight hours. The funeral can then be organised over the casket and there would be no need for a funeral director, hearse or limos, no hard sell on coffins and no big bill. Consider, the private crematoria could readily do this but no, like councils, they prefer to work for, and with, the funeral directors. It really is caveat corpus; body beware!

The good news is that the internet is increasing transparency and choice, which looks set to expand. Innovative individuals and anonymous large firms are advertising direct funerals, mostly cremation based, anywhere in the UK and at fixed costs.

R.I.P. Off! illustrates that funeral costs could be reduced if input, that is, staff time, could be cut out. Conversely, funeral directing wants to make funerals unduly complex so that their services are increasingly necessary, and more expensive. Ideally, everybody should have access to a council advisory service, face to face and not just via the internet, and support, up to the point where they could manage the funeral themselves; the DIY or Independent option. It's often the shortage of local advice, of able bodied bearers and a vehicle to carry a coffin that frustrates people taking this route. Sadly, even at Carlisle, where the novel is based, the council no longer stock coffins and the council website does not mention the reusable Carlisle Coffin, even though I am told it is still available. At the very least, the council who puts the bereaved first will have adopted the Institute of Cemetery & Crematorium Management (ICCM) Charter for the Bereaved, which was written by the author. This requires skill and commitment, and guarantees minimum advice and support, not least for Independent (DIY) funerals. It is this factor that probably results in so few private crematoria adopting the Charter.

In case you think that little people don't change things, I would ask you to think again. Over two hundred and fifty natural burial sites now handle 7% of the market (2012) and cremation faces an uncertain future. Little people, such as Joan Wood in the novel, which is her real name, and other advocates, most of whom are women, are making inroads – and the British way of death is the most innovative in the world. Even so, most people experiencing a death still automatically telephone a funeral director, leave the arrangements entirely to them and never mention the price.

That has ensured that competitive pricing is still rare, and the cost of funerals continues to increase well above inflation.

As for those on benefits, it is apparent that fewer people are receiving help through the Social Fund and funeral poverty is on the increase. In one case, this involved a man having to pay for his late mother's funeral over twenty years. For those with a poor credit rating, the men in black will demand a cash deposit. What they won't do is advise you how to do a low cost funeral without them – it's a rip off! You can fight back and if you want to know more about funerals then *www.goodfuneralguide.co.uk* (and book) by Charles Cowling will open all the doors you require. The Natural Death Centre *www.naturaldeath.org.uk* (Helpline 01962 712 690) supports those wanting to be in control of the funeral, and especially those seeking a green funeral. For those who want to study the subject, then in Chapter 30 'Death Unstung' Graham read a book called 'Natural Burial, Traditional – Secular Spiritualities and Funeral Innovation', and it changed his outlook. The authors are Douglas Davies and Hannah Rumble and it is published by Continuum. A coalition called 'Dying Matters' aims to change public knowledge, attitudes and behaviour towards death, dying and bereavement: see *www.dyingmatters.org*. An innovative funeral director in Bradford manufactures re-usable coffins for supply to any funeral director or council and an internet search on 'coffin covers' will locate this product.

My final comment is a sad little story! A friend of the author visited a small cemetery in Surrey in July 2011. She went with the daughter, whose mother was buried there a few years previously, and for whom they had dedicated a memorial seat. They felt it would be spiritually good to take a picnic, sit together on the seat, eat, and allow the deceased to participate however they might. A jobsworth spoiled it, reminding them that the rules, anonymous until that moment, prohibited eating food in the cemetery. They left, their way of grieving ruined by insensitivity, by parochial ignorance; by somebody who had not read this book. Perhaps the title should be changed to – S.O.D. Off!

Glossary

Agnostic – person who prays every day that they are right

Atheist – soulless existence, similar to a dog

At rest – calm before the account arrives

Baby-boomers – consequences of post-war rationing of condoms

Bearer – man with a shoulder pad (traditionally rarely a woman)

Burger-boomer – where six bearers are needed instead of four

Chapel of Repose – a room in which you view someone you do not
    recognise

Coffin – a very cheap box expensively veneered

Corpse couture – clothes to die for

Crack – gossip in Cumbria

Cremation – subtle process for transferring teeth amalgam into
    North Sea cod

Deaconess – church cleaner or cake maker masquerading as a vicar

Death – ultimate leisure

DIY funeral – funeral arranged by a woman; with balls

Embalming – the art of turning the benign into the toxic, sometimes
    referred to as pinking up

Funeral directing – the art of benevolence followed by a bill

Gratuities – money to buy acquiescence or: somebody else's finger
    up your arse

Hearse – a car with two bodies

Heaven – a place where you can't find a funeral director

Natural burial – kicking up the daises

Obituary – trite write or: the only time your other half ignores your faults

Package funeral – we know what you want better than you do

Pauper – derogatory Victorian name for somebody who could not afford a funeral; which is most of us now!

Pinking up – chemical infusion so that the corpse looks really healthy

Postmortem – handling organs excessively but without arousal

Pot mum – rabbit food masquerading as a pot of chrysanthemums on a grave

Purgatory – God's waiting room or: having your query transferred to a call centre in India

Rigor mortis – temporary stiffening, often experienced by men over sixty

R.I.P. – Regularly Increased Prices

Shroud (burial) – the only wool garment in which you expect to feel cold

Shroud (coffin) – glitzy backless garment, would be loved by Barbara Cartland fans

Vicar – the stranger taking the funeral service

Will – a means of letting your partner know you had a lover

Woodland burial – Nirvana for tree huggers

PV C6

The crack - 43